W9-ABH-443

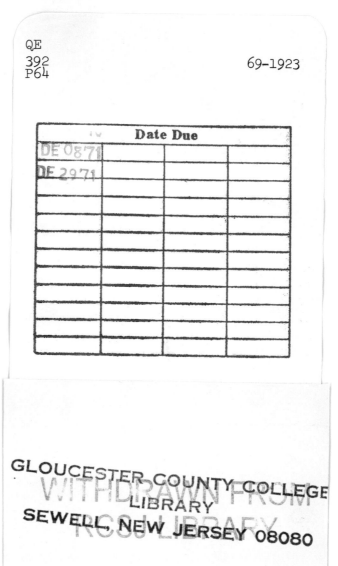

The Story
of
GEMS
and
semiprecious
stones

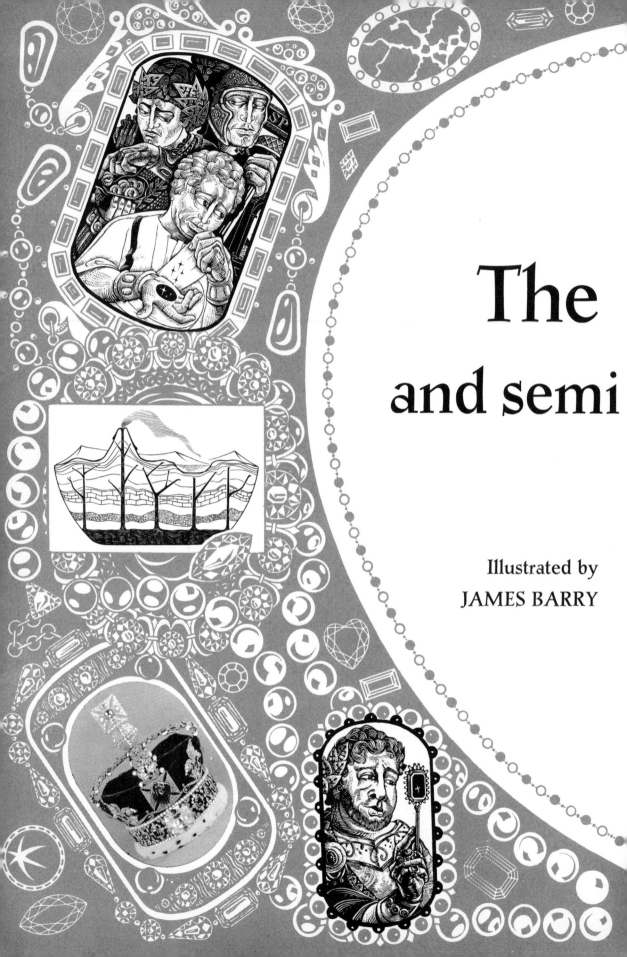

The

and semi

Illustrated by
JAMES BARRY

Story of Gems

precious stones

by FREDERICK H. POUGH

HARVEY HOUSE INC. Publishers
Irvington-on-Hudson, New York

A Story of Science Series Book

ACKNOWLEDGEMENTS AND CREDITS

The author is deeply indebted to JOSEPH ALVAREZ for his careful revision of the original manuscript. "THE STORY OF GEMS AND SEMIPRECIOUS STONES" has greatly benefited from his valuable contributions to its final form.

All photographs not otherwise credited are from the collection of the author.

Color photographs in the insert are by courtesy of:

The Controller of Her Britannic Majesty's Stationery Office, British Crown Copyright

The Smithsonian Institution

Ted Nichols Photography, Tucson, Arizona

CONTENTS

1. The Fascination of Gemstones

ON A HOT SUMMER DAY in 1701, a poor native, sifting pebbles in an Indian diamond mine, found one of the world's most famous diamonds. Of course, it did not yet look like a gem. A rough diamond, before it is cut and polished, is a dull stone. But this stone was the size of a small plum—the largest diamond the native ever had seen. At once he knew it was valuable.

He decided to smuggle it out of the mine. If he could sell it, he would be rich and would never again need to wade in the river shallows looking for other men's diamonds.

The risk was great because the penalty for stealing diamonds was severe. It he were caught, he might never be seen again. But the native had visions of great wealth. So at the end of the day, he made a deep cut in his calf, slipped the stone into the wound and wrapped a cloth around his leg. Then he limped to the guard at the gate.

His plan worked. When he was out of the mine, the man headed for the nearest port city, where he hoped to sell the diamond. But by the time he reached the coast, he was so afraid of being caught with the stone that he sold it to a ship's captain for free passage to "a distant land."

The captain did not keep his bargain. Once out to sea, he had the native thrown overboard. Then, for $5,000, he sold the rough diamond to an Indian merchant, who promptly sold it to Sir Thomas Pitt, the English Governor at Madras, for $100,000!

Sir Thomas had the stone cut and polished. The finished gem was less than half as large as the rough diamond. But it was so beautiful that the Duke of Orleans, the French Regent, bought it from Sir Thomas for $600,000! Thus did the Regent diamond, as the gem was now called, pass from a humble Indian miner to the powerful ruler of France.

During the French Revolution the crown jewels were stolen. Several weeks after the theft, the Regent diamond was found in a ditch in the Champs-Elysées in France! The gem was so well known that the thieves had not been able to sell it.

The Republican government took over the valuable diamond. Later it was mounted in the hilt of Napoleon's state sword. If you ever go to France, you may see it in the famous Louvre Museum.

The Regent or Pitt diamond, a fine white stone of 140 carats. Now in the Louvre with the French crown jewels.

The value of gemstones lies in their combination of beauty, hardness, and rarity. Also of interest to us is how the gemstones are formed and cut, where they are found, the special way they bend, or *refract*, light and how some of them change colors. The study of all this is called *gemmology*, or the science of gems. It is what we will be talking about in this book.

Money, Magic and Beauty

Most people think of gems in terms of money. They call diamonds, emeralds, rubies, sapphires, and pearls "precious," and just about everything else "semiprecious." But such terms no longer have any meaning.

A window of Tiffany & Company, New York jewelers.

For example, a fine "semiprecious" aquamarine may be more valuable than a flawed, or defective, "precious" emerald.

Until recently people believed that gemstones had magical powers. You may have heard that the opal, a gem which flashes the colors of the rainbow, is "unlucky." Jade, a green stone, was thought to cure pains in the side. In fact, the name "jade" comes from the Spanish *piedra de ijada*, which means "stone of the side." One medieval medicine included among

Medieval physician using a bloodstone to cure nosebleed. From the "Hortus Sanitatis," Strassburg, c. 1483.

its thirty-four ingredients emerald, sapphire, topaz, pearl, garnet, ruby, amber and coral. This "most noble" elixir was supposed to cure anything. One suspects it transported unhappy patients right out of this world.

Such superstitions led to the use of birthstones. Each month had a special birthstone. For example, the birthstone for May was emerald. This gem was supposed to have special powers for a person born in May.

16

The tradition of birthstones was strong—so strong that it led to naming two stones for October. The first was opal, but people worried about having an "unlucky" birthstone. So, fairly recently, tourmaline, a lovely gem which is found in many colors, was also named a birthstone for October.

Here are the months and their birthstones:

January—Garnet	June—Pearl,	September—Sapphire
February—Amethyst	Moonstone, or	October—Opal or
March—Aquamarine	Alexandrite	Tourmaline
April—Diamond	July—Ruby	November—Topaz
May—Emerald	August—Peridot or	December—Turquoise or
	Sardonyx	Zircon

A *gemmologist*—a person who specializes in the study of gems—looks at stones differently, critically. He considers how near a stone comes to being what is considered the finest quality of its kind. How clear is it? How big is it? Is it genuine? How well is it cut? Is its color perfect? When you finish this book, I hope that you will know some of the things a gemmologist looks for.

When a Ruby is Not a Ruby

If you saw ring with a red gemstone in it in a jeweler's window, you probably would think, "That's a ruby." Most of us identify gemstones by their color. But if you are not a gemmologist, the colors of stones can be very confusing. Perhaps you have heard the familiar rhyme:

Rubies are red,
Sapphires are blue,
Diamonds are nice
And imitations won't do.

The rhyme is useful as far as it goes. But when you see a good museum's collection of gems, you will find that not only are rubies red but so are some spinels, garnets, tourmalines and even diamonds.

Well, you might say, how *can* you tell the difference between one gem and another? There are special tests for this, and some of them will be described later. Actually, a gemmologist learns to recognize the slight difference between the red of a ruby and the reds of garnet and tourmaline. It is not always easy. One of the most famous of England's crown jewels, the Black Prince's ruby, which dates back to 1366, is not a ruby at all but a spinel!

Animal, Mineral or Vegetable?

There are many kinds of gemstones, and later I will describe them one by one. The important thing to remember here is that all gemstones fall into two classes: *natural* and *man-made*.

Natural gem substances include *minerals*, such as diamonds, jade and quartz, and *organic* substances—that is, substances which come from living plants or animals—such as pearls, amber and coral.

Most gemstones are minerals. There are over two thousand minerals. But only about twenty of these are beautiful, hard, and rare, yet accessible enough to be gemstones.

2. What is a Mineral?

MINERALS ARE ALL AROUND US. Our Earth is composed of rocks, rocks are composed of minerals, and minerals are composed of natural "elements," such as oxygen, carbon, aluminum and silicon.

Some minerals consist of only one element. Diamonds, for example, are 100% carbon. But most minerals are *compounds*—chemical combinations of two or more elements. Quartz, for example, the most common mineral, is a compound of silicon and oxygen.

Ninety-two different elements have been found in minerals. These elements combine chemically with each other in different ways. Oxygen and silicon make quartz. When oxygen combines with aluminum, the result is corundum, a mineral which is called a ruby when red and a sapphire when blue.

In *mineralogy*, the science of minerals, these chemical combinations are important; they help *mineralogists* understand why some minerals will melt at low temperatures and others at high, why some minerals will dissolve in water and others will not. They also help mineralogists understand a mineral's physical properties or characteristics, such as color and hardness. Some chemical combinations make soft minerals, others make hard minerals. Only the hard ones are gemstones.

How Hard Is Hard?

It is difficult to state just how hard any one mineral is. In 1822 a German mineralogist, Friedrich Mohs, devised a way to measure the hardness of minerals *in relation to each other*. He chose ten minerals—out of hundreds—that seemed to be separated by about equal degrees of hardness and gave them numbers:

1. Talc   2. Gypsum   3. Calcite   4. Fluorite   5. Apatite
6. Feldspar   7. Quartz   8. Topaz   9. Corundum 10. Diamond

Talc is the softest mineral and diamond is the hardest. In Mohs' scale, a mineral with a higher number will scratch a mineral with a lower number. With a topaz, for instance, you could scratch any mineral from 1-7, but you could not scratch corundum or diamond.

Mineralogists now know, through a modern machine called a *sclerometer* (from the Greek *scleros*: hard, and *metron*: measure), that the differences in hardness in Mohs' scale are not equal. For example, the diamond (10)—the hardest substance in the world—is so much harder than corundum (9), that in another type of test diamond is 8000, corundum about 2000.

To judge the hardness of minerals, try rubbing first halite (common salt), and then sand, between two pieces of glass. The halite will crumble; the sand will scratch the glass.

But the Mohs' scale is still very useful. With it, you can measure the relative hardness of any mineral. You would find, for instance, that chromite, a compound of chromium and oxygen, scratches apatite (5) but not feldspar (6). So chromite is said to have a hardness of 5½.

You can do this with any substance. Your fingernail has a hardness of 2 plus—it will scratch talc (1) and gypsum (2) but not calcite (3). A penny has a hardness of 3 plus, a penknife 5 plus, and glass 5½.

You can see for yourself the difference in hardness between minerals if you rub first halite—common salt—and then sand between two pieces of glass. The halite, which has a hardness of 2, will crumble. But the sand, which is mostly ground quartz (7), will scratch the glass.

Crystal But Not Always Clear

Almost all minerals form *crystals*—symmetrical block shapes bounded by flat surfaces called *faces*. And these crystals take one of six basic shapes:

(*Diamond*) CUBIC (all sides alike)	(*Zircon*) TETRAGONAL (four sides alike)	(*Beryl*) HEXAGONAL (six sides alike)
(*Topaz*) ORTHORHOMBIC (Three unequal sides, all right angles)	(*Diopside*) MONOCLINIC (Three unequal sides, 16 of 24 right angles)	(*Labradorite*) TRICLINIC (Three unequal sides, no right angles)

These shapes are actually large scale models of the kind of pattern in which the *atoms*—the smallest particles of an element—of a mineral are arranged. These patterns are very important. You will remember that the diamond is 100% carbon. So is graphite, the soft mineral which provides the "lead" for your pencils. Why are they so different—one hard and transparent, the other soft and opaque? Because their atoms are arranged differently.

You can see the difference in the photo shown on p. 23. The carbon atoms form a cube in the diamond and a hexagon in graphite. In the cubic structure, the carbon atoms are more closely packed together, and this accounts for the extreme hardness of diamonds.

SIX BASIC CRYSTAL SHAPES

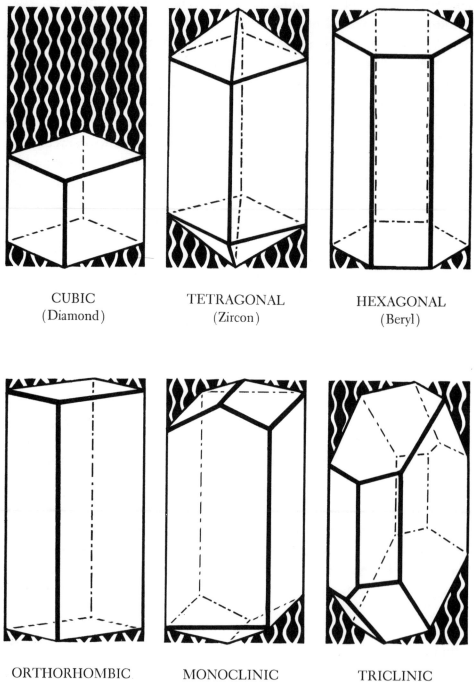

CUBIC
(Diamond)

TETRAGONAL
(Zircon)

HEXAGONAL
(Beryl)

ORTHORHOMBIC
(Topaz)

MONOCLINIC
(Diopside)

TRICLINIC
(Labradorite)

The arrangement of atoms in a mineral also determines how it will *cleave*, or split into smooth plane surfaces. In many minerals, the atoms are closer together and more strongly attracted to each other in one direction than in another. So it will break apart more easily along the plane of the weaker direction. Have you ever peeled flakes off a piece of mica? You can cleave it almost indefinitely in one direction, but not at all in the other. This is an important factor in the cutting of gemstones. The diamond, for example, cleaves easily only in one direction, and the gem cutter must be careful to select the right one. If he chooses a wrong direction, the diamond may *fracture*—break into jagged, uneven pieces, like glass. When the Culinan diamond—the largest ever found—was cut into gemstones, experts spent nine months just deciding how to cleave it!

Most minerals do not cleave at all, they only fracture. Among gemstones that do not cleave easily are beryl—the mineral name for emerald and aquamarine—opal, quartz, spinel and tourmaline. Since they are so much softer than diamond, they can be sawn apart or ground down in any direction.

CUBE STRUCTURES OF GRAPHITE AND DIAMOND

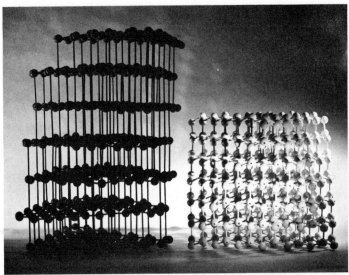

Wide-spaced layers of carbon atoms in graphite make it soft, opaque, and easy to flake. The compact structure of carbon atoms in the diamond make it the hardest mineral known, and transparent.

23

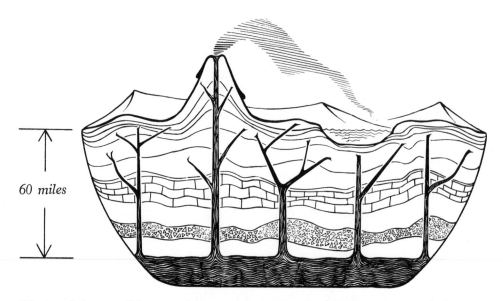

60 miles

The earth has a solid crust of stone at least 60 miles thick. A volcano is created when the magma (molten, gas-charged rock) breaks through the earth's surface. When it hardens and cools it is called intrusive lava.

3. How Gem Minerals Form

SOME MINERALS—even some gem minerals—are forming even as you read this. The formation of minerals is a continual process which is closely linked with how rocks are formed and how they are destroyed, how they harden and how they break up and are eroded, or worn away.

There are hundreds of different rocks, but they all fall into three basic groups—igneous (from the Latin *ignis*: fire), *sedimentary*, and *metamorphic* (from the Greek *meta*: change, and *morph*: form). Each group is formed in a different way.

Igneous Rocks: the Gem Makers

The Earth has a solid crust of stone at least sixty miles thick. We think the material beneath this crust is *molten*, or dough-like. From time to time, a column of *magma*—molten, gas-charged rock—works its way up through the crust. When it breaks out on the Earth's surface, a volcano is created, and the magma that flows over the sides is called *lava*. The lava is made up of minerals, but the melted rock cools and

24

hardens so quickly that the individual grains do not have time to grow very large.

Usually the magma does not break through the Earth's surface. As it eats its way up through the cooler rocks of the crust, the molten liquid loses heat and begins to harden. When it hardens near the Earth's surface, it is called *intrusive* lava. It usually cools in thin seams called *dikes*, which cut across the formations of rock in the crust.

Although the stiffening magma is trapped, its gases continue to escape through crevices, or cracks, in the rock crust in much the same way gas escapes from a bottle of soda pop when you loosen the cap. These gases—steam is one of the main ones—carry along elements from the magma. As the vapors cool, they often deposit these elements on the sides of the rock crevices in *veins*. Many metal ore minerals, such as pyrite, the yellowish, metallic iron mineral called "fools' gold," are often formed this way.

When the magma hardens and is trapped at a greater depth, usually in larger masses, it forms what we call *plutonic* rocks. (Pluto was the Greek god of the underworld, the world of the dead.) Plutonic rock is a valuable source of minerals because its magma cools very slowly, giving the mineral crystals more time to grow. What happens is that a crystal-liquid mush, like freezing milk, forms, and as it is pressed into a more compact mass of small crystals, the still fluid residue is squeezed out and escapes through a crevice which the stiff magma could not get into. The fluid residue allows a freer wandering of the elements, so they can crystallize slower into coarser crystals. If most of the elements are non-stony, they may leave an open water or gas-filled pocket into which crystals can grow without interference, free to assume the shape best suited to them.

Slow cooling rocks, including those from which the gases have been squeezed, are mineral aggregates and are called coarse-grained rocks. Granite, a coarse-grained rock, is the most common plutonic rock. A very coarse type of granite, called pegmatite (from the Greek *pegma*: joined together) dikes, is one of our most important sources of gem minerals. It is crystallized in long crevices called pegmatite dikes. Beryl, topaz, quartz, garnet, and tourmaline are among the gemstones found in pegmatite dikes. Often, an excess of liquids leaves an open space in the pegmatite dike, where the last crystals can grow without interference.

4,000 Million Years of Gem Making

If you are wondering how stones in once deep rock formations now can be found near the Earth's surface, you will find the answer in *geology*, the study of the Earth's crust. The oldest rocks on our Earth's surface, *geologists* have found, are 4,000 million years old! During that time, thick portions of the Earth's crust have been folded then pushed up into mountain ranges. As they eroded, the soil of their summits was redeposited as sediment, to be pressed down by the weight of further layers of sediment and then, perhaps, was folded again. The process is continual, ever repeating, ever renewing.

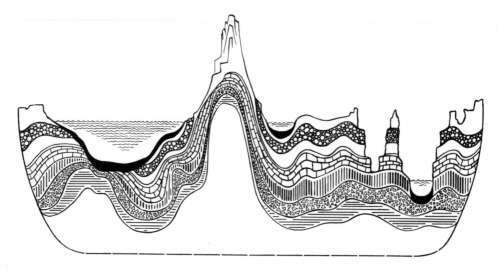

In the last 4,000 million years thick portions of the earth's crust have been folded and pushed up into mountain ranges. As they eroded the soil of their summits was redeposited as sediment.

As soon as a rock is exposed, air and water begin to *weather* it—that is, the oxygen of the air and water combine chemically with minerals, or with elements in the minerals, and the minerals break apart and are swept away. Some of the elements dissolve in the water and are carried deeper into fresh rock. There they may separate from the water and, with one or more elements of the fresh rock, form a second mineral in crevices. Turquoise is formed this way. It is a compound of copper from one mineral, aluminum from another, and phosphorus from a third.

26

Such "secondary" minerals as turquoise are never found buried deeply. The water which bears the elements for their formation finds the rock too compact before it can sink very far below the surface.

Some elements and minerals resist weathering better than others. But, in time, all exposed rocks are eroded by the action of streams, wind, ice, frost, and heat. Weathering and erosion help bring our gem deposits to the surface by wearing away the overlying rocks which once covered the pegmatite dikes. Most of our gemstones come from tropical countries, like Brazil and India, where the weathering is deep, and one can dig easily into the once hard rock.

Sedimentary and Metamorphic Rocks

Rock is broken down into soil by weathering. Some of that soil is eroded away by streams and rivers, eventually to be deposited as sediment in river deltas, mud flats, valley floors or ocean beds. Over millions of years, one layer of sediment is deposited on top of another, and in ocean basins the weight of the successive layers presses them together, eventually hardening them into sedimentary rocks. Much of the United States is underlain by sedimentary rocks, showing that at one time portions of the continent were under water, but since have been raised.

You may find fossils—the preserved remains or imprint of living creatures—but you will not find many gemstones in sedimentary rocks. Some of the few that do form there are opal and varieties of quartz, a very common compound which is formed in all three classes of rocks.

However, sedimentary rocks can be a stage in the formation of many gemstones, for eventually crustal movements with great heat and pressure can change the weak beds of weathered fragments into harder metamorphic rocks, where many gemstones are found.

Metamorphic and igneous rocks, since they are created under similar temperature and pressure conditions, often look alike and contain many of the same minerals. Corundum, garnet, spinel, sometimes even tourmaline, zircon, and, of course, quartz, are some of the gemstones that can be formed in both metamorphic and igneous rocks. Lazurite, the

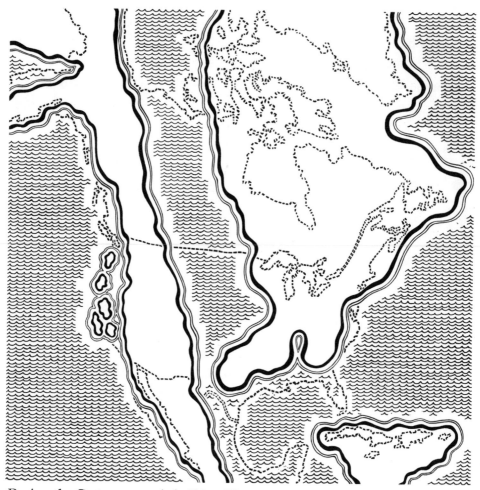

During the Cretaceous period, 120 million years ago, much of what is now the United States was under water.

mineral name for lapis lazuli, a lovely bluish gemstone, is formed only in metamorphic rocks.

Most gemstones found today were formed millions of years ago in rocks crystallized from magmas that cooled deep within the Earth's crust. They have slowly risen to the Earth's surface under the influence of powerful forces. The 1964 Alaskan earthquake will give you an idea of just how powerful these forces are. It was perhaps the worst earthquake ever recorded, and very destructive, yet it shifted the Earth's crust along its *fault*, or fracture line, only a few feet. Think what force it took to lift the rocks to form a mountain range like the Rockies!

28

Diamond cutting and polishing in 1730, showing a diamond cutter's wheel or mill.

4. From Gemstone to Jewel

HAVE YOU EVER FOUND smooth, pretty stones in a stream or at the sea-shore? Such colored *opaque* stones—stones through which light cannot pass—almost certainly were man's first gemstones. Jewels from ancient Egypt, Greece, and Rome are mainly colored quartz stones like jasper and agate. The ancient Chinese prized jade.

Transparent stones—stones through which light can pass—did not become popular until man learned to cut and polish them. Such work is done by a *lapidary* (from the Latin *lapidarius:* of stone).

Shaping a Jewel

Gems are cut into several shapes. The simplest is the cabochon, which looks like half of a marble or a low dome. Almost all gems were cut *en cabochon* until the fourteenth century, when lapidaries learned to cut facets, or flat faces, on gemstones. Opaque stones and translucent

COURTESY OF LAPIDARY JOURNAL AND 3M COMPANY

Cutting cabochon stones by hand with diamond disks. The stones are mounted on "dops" to facilitate holding them against the lap (a fast-spinning wheel), which is coated with an abrasive mud.

stones—stones which are partly transparent—are still cut en cabochon because this shape best brings out their beauty after they are polished.

Sometimes a transparent stone—a ruby, for instance—is cut en cabochon, but clear stones are usually cut in *brilliant* or *step-cut* style.

30

DIAMOND—BRILLIANT-CUT (ROUND)

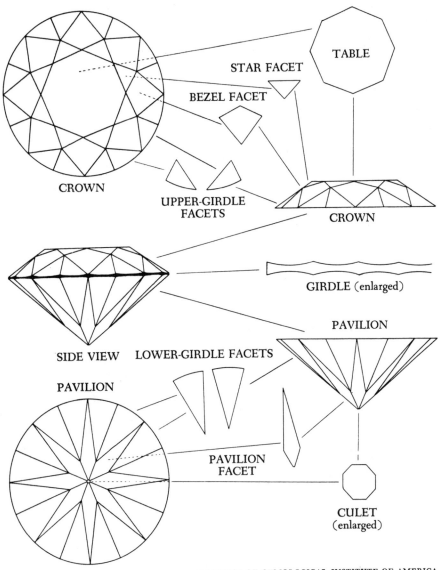

STAR FACET

TABLE

BEZEL FACET

CROWN

UPPER-GIRDLE
FACETS

CROWN

GIRDLE (enlarged)

PAVILION

SIDE VIEW   LOWER-GIRDLE FACETS

PAVILION

PAVILION
FACET

CULET
(enlarged)

As you can see in the illustration, the usual brilliant looks like a truncated, or shortened, double cone on which a series of triangular facets have been cut. The top facet is called the *table* and the bottom facet is called the *culet*. Fifty-eight facets are cut on the upper and lower slopes of the gem—thirty-two plus the table above the girdle (where the cones meet) and twenty-four plus the culet below it. Diamonds and light-colored stones like zircon are often cut as brilliants because this style gives them "sparkle" and "fire."

Several modifications of brilliants are illustrated below. The shape of the stone, particularly if it is a costly one, often depends on the shape of the rough piece.

In the step-cut, the series of facets are long rectangles or "steps" which cover the bottom and top of the stone. Emeralds and aquamarines are usually step-cut because this style of cut enriches their color.

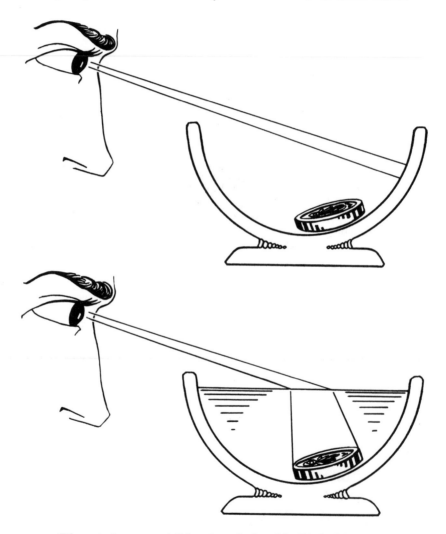

The coin becomes visible when the bowl is filled with water.

32

Bending Light Around Corners

Have you ever wondered why a diamond has more "sparkle" and "fire" than glass in the same brilliant shape? The reason lies in the greater ability of the diamond to refract, or bend, light.

All transparent substances refract light as it passes through them. You can see this for yourself in a simple experiment. Put a penny in the bottom of a shallow bowl and place the bowl on a table. Then gradually lower your line of sight until you no longer can see the penny over the rim of the bowl. Now have a friend fill the bowl with water. Without changing your position, you will be able to see the penny again because the water has bent the light rays so that they strike the coin.

Although all transparent substances refract light, some refract it more than others. The exact amount of refraction of a substance can be calculated with the aid of a *refractometer* (remember, meter means to measure) . It is expressed in a number called the *index of refraction*. How that number is obtained is not important here. It is enough to know that for most transparent minerals the index of refraction is low. For air it is 1, and it is 1.33 for water, 1.55 for glass, and only 1.58 for the emerald. But for the diamond it is 2.42, and for some clear synthetic compounds it is even higher.

So a diamond bends light almost twice as much as water and half again as much as glass. This is because the atoms in a diamond slow down the speed of light more than the atoms in water or glass do. And they do this because they are packed so closely together.

The facets of a brilliant cut diamond are angled to take advantage of the diamond's high index of refraction. They are cut at an angle—about 35° on top and about 41° below—so that the light which comes in from the top of the gem will not "leak" out through the sides or the bottom but will be reflected back through the top. This is what gives a diamond its sparkle.

Glass sparkles less because even when it is cut in the brilliant style it does not refract light enough to trap it all and return it through the top facets; some leaks out through the sides and bottom of the glass.

And now you see that emeralds are step-cut to emphasize color instead of brightness because with their low index of refraction (1.58) they cannot make a sparkling brilliant.

STEPS IN CUTTING A DIAMOND

The rough diamond may be shown in a diagram as an octahedron.

The octahedron is sawed in two, a little above its middle.

After rounding or girdling the diamond looks like this. The flat top is its table; the circumference is its girdle.

Here the diamond has four main facets above the girdle (two in front and two behind) and four main facets below the girdle.

The stone now has eight facets above the girdle and eight more below it. This is like the 17-facet "single cut" diamond.

The brillianteerer has here cut additional facets on the stone, approaching the fully cut diamond with 58 facets.

COURTESY OF N. W. AYER & SON, INC.

POPULAR DIAMOND SHAPES

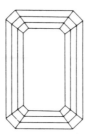

MARQUISE   EMERALD CUT   PEAR SHAPE   OVAL

SINGLE CUT   BAGUETTE

COURTESY OF N. W. AYER & SON, INC.

34

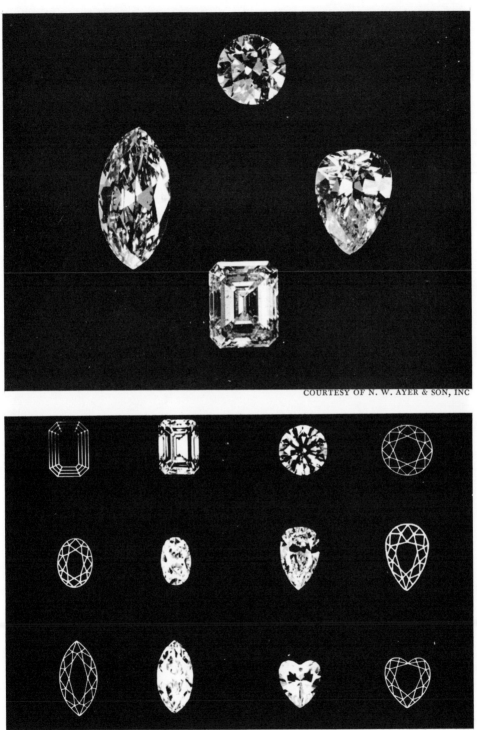

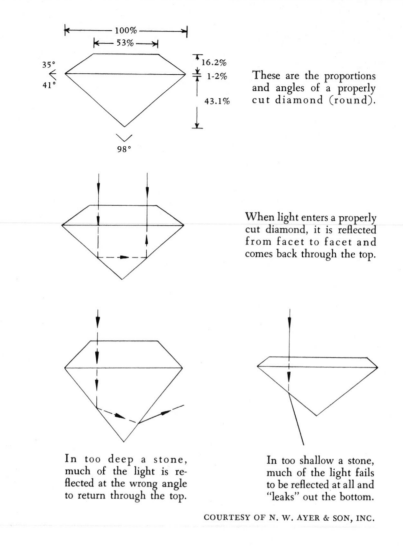

These are the proportions and angles of a properly cut diamond (round).

When light enters a properly cut diamond, it is reflected from facet to facet and comes back through the top.

In too deep a stone, much of the light is reflected at the wrong angle to return through the top.

In too shallow a stone, much of the light fails to be reflected at all and "leaks" out the bottom.

COURTESY OF N. W. AYER & SON, INC.

When a lapidary cuts facets on a gemstone, he varies the angle depending upon the stone's index of refraction. The facets on a diamond are fairly shallow, but the facets on clear quartz, which has a refractive index of only 1.54, must be much steeper. Even at best, as with glass, some of the light will escape through the bottom and sides.

All clear gemstones are either *singly* or *doubly* refracting. The difference is really quite simple if you remember what you read about crystals in Chapter II. Diamond, spinel, and garnet are singly refracting because their crystals belong to the cubic, or "isometric," system and light entering any face of the crystal will be equally slowed and uniformly bent by the interference from the mineral's atoms. Substances that have no regular arrangement of their atoms and do not form crystals, like glass, water, plastic, as well as gemstone opal, are also singly refracting.

A gem is doubly refracting when the top and side faces of its crystals are unlike—as they are in all crystal systems except the cubic. Light entering the crystal from its top face may find the mineral's atoms packed closely together. Light entering the same crystal from a side face may find the mineral's atoms spaced further apart. So the light passing from top to bottom is slowed down more than the light going from one side to the other, giving the stone double refraction or two different amounts of bending and slowing.

To find out if a cut stone is singly or doubly refracting, all you need is a white card and sunlight. Hold the stone with its table facing the sun. Hold the card about six inches away from the stone. Then turn the stone

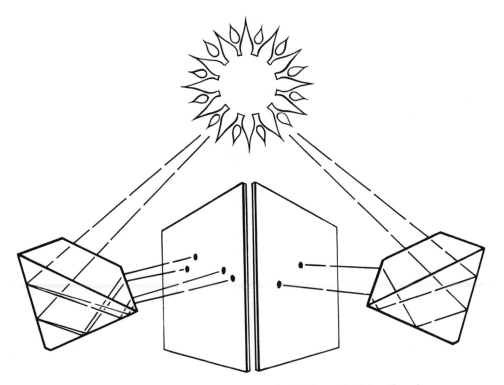

An experiment to determine if a stone is singly or doubly refracting.

until internal reflections of the sunlight shine on the card. From each back facet a singly refracting stone will reflect one spot on the card; a doubly refracting stone will reflect double spots.

Testing a stone for single or double refraction is a way to distinguish between, say, a spinel and a ruby of the same color. A stone's actual index of refraction is another way of identifying it.

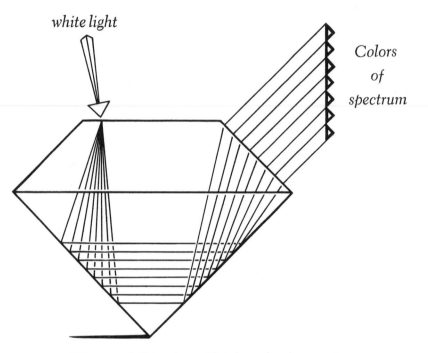

Diagram of dispersion with prism, showing spectrum.

Breaking White Light Into Rainbow Colors

Ordinary light, though it looks white, is really a mixture of colors. You can demonstrate this for yourself by passing a beam of light through a glass prism. What was white light is spread out into its different parts, or *wavelengths*, the technical term for the formula that describes the vibration frequency of each color as it speeds through space.

The separation of light into various colors is known as *dispersion*. Dispersion is related to refraction; in fact, it is a kind of refraction. Each color has its own index of refraction, and sometimes the differences between these indices are great.

38

Some transparent substances disperse, or spread, light more than others. A substance with a high index of refraction is likely to combine it with a strong dispersion because the two properties are related. The stronger the dispersion the wider the colors will spread, and the more visible to the naked eye will be its "rainbow" hues. This is what gives some gemstones their "fire"—a combination of high refraction and strong dispersion. A diamond is more fiery than glass—and most gems—because it combines a higher index of refraction than most, with a stronger dispersion than most. Next time you see a diamond, look for the flashes of rainbow colors in the stone. Now you know what causes them.

The Finishing Touches

The lapidary cleans and shapes a rough stone by grinding it on a wheel containing a coarse grit of diamond dust or of silicon carbide, a hard artificial abrasive. Then he cements the stone to a short stick called a *dop* stick. The final cutting and polishing of the stone is done on a *lap*, a fast-spinning flat metal wheel mounted on a table. The stone, stuck

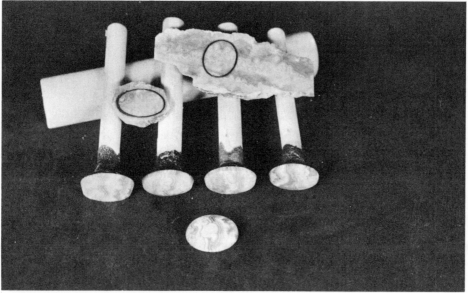

COURTESY OF LAPIDARY JOURNAL

Three steps for finishing cabochons: Marking slab, four gems mounted on dop sticks after a shaping which grinds the edges smooth, and a finished, rounded-top cabochon.

to one end of the dop stick, is pressed down on the lap, which is wet with a mixture containing an abrasive compound. The professional cutter then inserts the other end of the dop stick into one of a series of little holes in an upright board fixed at the edge of the table. This board is called the *jam-peg*.

Often a different wheel and a different abrasive are used in each stage of the cutting and polishing of a stone. The shaping grit is coarse and is followed by a finer grit which smooths off the facets to prepare it for the fine dust that gives the final polish.

The lapidary's art takes long practice and skill, for the inclination of each facet of a gem must be exactly right and uniform so that each facet will meet the others precisely at a point at the center. There are various mechanical aids for measuring these inclinations, but the professional lapidary seldom uses them; he judges the angles by eye. There is no room for error. Diamond cutters have even more problems because the diamond is so hard. Diamond cutters usually cut no other stones, only diamonds.

When a gem is finished, it is taken off the dop and weighed. The standard unit of weight for gemstones is the *carat*, a unit that is thought to have originated from the weight of the seed of a locust tree—*Ceratonia siliqua*, which is widely scattered throughout India. Today, one carat equals 200 milligrams, so five carats equal one gram.

The finished gem may weigh only a fifth as much as the original piece of rough stone. It depends on the shape of the rough, how perfect its interior, and sometimes, how rare the stone is. American and European lapidaries often sacrifice weight for symmetry, but Oriental lapidaries almost always cut a stone to preserve all possible weight and color.

Now that you know what makes a mineral a gemstone, how they form and how they are cut and polished, it is time to turn to the individual stones themselves.

COURTESY OF DR. E. GÜBELIN

Washing gem-bearing gravels down a sluice in Mogok, Burma. The residue of pebbles is hand-sorted for the valuable gemmy bits.

5. Ruby, Sapphire and Spinel

RUBIES AND SAPPHIRES are known as "the jewels of kings." These precious stones are set in the gold and silver of countless royal crowns, sword hilts, brooches and rings. Long ago, people thought that rubies and sapphires protected them against all sorts of bad luck, even demons and poisons. The stones didn't do this, of course, but they were beautiful to look at, and still are.

Ruby and sapphire are the gem names for the mineral, corundum. Pure corundum is colorless, a crystallized compound of aluminum and oxygen. As a gemstone it is worth little. It is the intrusion of a tiny chemical "impurity" in the corundum that creates the rich red of a ruby and the cornflower blue of a sapphire. In the ruby, the impurity is in the form of chromium oxide; in the sapphire, it is iron and titanium oxide. Spinel, a magnesium-aluminum oxide, is not related to corundum, but some of the red spinels look so like rubies that until mineral study became a science, the difference between the two was not clearly understood.

The Most Valuable Jewel

Large rubies are the rarest and most valuable commercial jewels in the world. But rubies never are very large. Even the largest weigh only

30 to 40 carats—about a tenth the weight of the biggest diamond. Few unflawed rubies are found that weigh over five carats. Very small rubies, however, are fairly abundant.

Rubies range in color from a yellowish to a bluish red. The rarest and loveliest stones are tinged with blue. These "pigeon-blood" rubies, as they are called, are found in hot, moist Burma, near the town of Mogok. For many years they were mined by a British company. But to get permission to mine the stones, the management had to promise to give the largest rubies to the Burmese King, who, not surprisingly, was known as "Lord of the Rubies." Eventually the mining operation was abandoned (as was the Burmese monarchy), and a lake now occupies the site of the old mine. But the nearby valley is still dotted with small diggings which yield a few stones each year.

Rubies also are found in Siam, Tanzania and Ceylon, a tropical island famous as a source of many gemstones. The typical Siamese ruby is a yellower red than the Burmese ruby and much darker. Jewelers consider it less valuable than the Burmese stone. Ceylonese rubies are paler than either Burmese or Siamese stones. The best African stones resemble those of Siam.

If you were to visit a ruby mine, you would find a lot of people sifting stones. Rubies are found as red pebbles in the gravels of stream

Ruby crystals imbedded in stone. Most sapphire crystals tend to be long and thin rather than tabular, as are ruby crystals.

42

beds or at the bottom of a thick layer of soil. To mine them, workers dig shafts down through the soil to the upper surface of the bedrock. Then they tunnel outwards in all directions as far as they dare, hoisting the earth and pebbles to the surface in baskets. During the rainy season, the natives wash and sift the gravel to pick out the gemstones.

You cannot scratch a ruby, which has a hardness of 9, with anything but a diamond or another ruby. Ruby has a high (1.77) index of refraction so it makes an attractive brilliant, though it is usually cut in the shape that saves most from the rough.

Corundum forms hexagonal (six-sided) crystals, but they may be long and thin, squat and barrel-shaped or even tabular (table-like). Ruby crystals are often tabular. Very flat and rather thin ruby crystals are found embedded in a green rock in one of the African occurrences, but only small gemstones have been cut fom them. Smaller, but similar, crystals are found in North Carolina, both embedded in rock and loose in gravel. Only a few gemstones have been cut from these crystals, but the deposit is open to the public, and for a fee, you may search for your own rubies.

And Sapphires Too

Sapphire is a blue corundum. An old superstition says that the mere sight of one will kill a spider. This isn't true, of course, but the sight of a lovely sapphire might win a lady's heart!

Rubies and sapphires often are found in the same gem deposits. Sapphires are more abundant than rubies, and some large sapphires weigh as much as several hundred carats. Most sapphire crystals are long and thin rather than tabular, as ruby crystals tend to be.

The most famous sapphires in the world come from Kashmir. This tiny country is crossed by the Zanskar range of the Himalayas, the high mountain wall which separates India from China. In 1881, there was a landslide on one of the Zanskar peaks. Rock and earth came tumbling down the mountain slope. When the dust had settled, it was discovered that the slide had uncovered a rich deposit of sapphires.

And what sapphires! Though they seemed clear, cutting showed that they were not completely transparent but were filled with micro-scopic, dust-like particles which made the gem glow softly. All over the

Blue sapphires range from pale to deep cornflower to inky blues.

world Kashmir sapphires became the standard against which other sapphires were measured.

The Kashmir deposit is no longer worked, but the finest sapphires still are called "Kashmirs," even though they now come from Siam or Burma. Meanwhile, guards patrol the slope of the mountain in Kashmir, to prevent unauthorized digging.

Sapphires are found in the United States, too. Montana has the best, but most are small, showing grey or steely blues, colors that are not good sapphire hues. If you have a very old "jewelled" watch, you may have some Montana sapphires in it. Because they are so durable, sapphires (and rubies) are used as bearings in watches and electrical instruments. These stones now are produced synthetically (see Chapter 17), but useful ones once came from Montana.

Years ago, a rare deposit of fine blue sapphires was discovered in Yogo Gulch, Montana. The gem crystals were embedded in a wide dike of volcanic rock, and the surface rock was so weathered and soft that it could be broken easily. A company was formed to mine the gems. However, once the soft surface rock was worked through, it became more difficult to extract the sapphires, for the fresh rock under the surface was still very hard.

Digging was halted temporarily. The miners were sure that after a year or two on the surface the newly exposed rock would also crumble and the sapphires would come out easily again. But it didn't, and thirty

44

years later, the Yogo Gulch rock still seems as hard as ever, and the mine is still closed.

Fancy Sapphires

Not all sapphires are blue. Some are yellow, green, pink, violet, orange and combinations of these hues. Just as titanium and iron oxide make corundum blue, other impurities create the other corundum colors. Such stones are called "fancy" sapphires. They come mainly from Ceylon, though a few are found in Montana and Australia. Light yellow probably is the most common color. The rarest is an orange-pink stone called *padparadschah*, which is valued very highly in the Orient.

Fancy sapphires, since they generally are light in color and (being corundum) have a high refraction, often can be cut into sparkling brilliants, though they usually come as asymmetrical "native cuts." They cost far less than rubies and sapphires, and make handsome jewels.

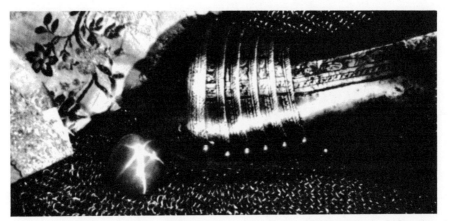

The Star of India, the largest blue star sapphire known (563 carats), belonging to the American Museum of Natural History. This was the major stone stolen in the highly publicized robbery of the Morgan collection in 1964.

Star Sapphires and Rubies

Crystallized impurities are sometimes distributed through a crystal while it forms. These impurities—which do not dissolve in the mineral, as chemical impurities do—are called *inclusions*. They may make a stone cloudy or flawed. But they also may be responsible for a different sort of gemstone. The randomly scattered microscopic inclusions in a "Kashmir" sapphire give this stone its special softly glowing quality. Often, however,

45

the inclusions that get into corundum form tiny needles which point in three different directions and reflections from them cross each other in a "star" pattern. The result is a star sapphire or star ruby. Star gemstones are called "phenomenal" stones, and they must be cut en cabochon to bring out their characteristic patterns.

You seldom see the ideal star stone. Its color must be rich but not too dark, and the star must be sharp but look as though it were inside the stone, not sliding over the surface. When there are too many included needles, the stone seems too opaque; but when there are not enough needles, the stone is too clear and its star looks weak. Finally, the "legs" of the star should run straight to the edge of the stone without a break.

Star sapphires and star rubies are found in Ceylon, Burma and Siam, in the same deposits as the clear corundum gemstones. Blue and grey are common star sapphire colors. The even more common and inexpensive black star sapphires—opaque-looking stones with bronze colored stars— are found in Siam and Australia. But no one has ever seen stars in most of the fancy sapphire colors; for some reason, there don't seem to be any yellow or orange stars.

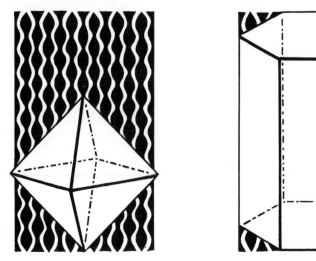

A spinel crystal (cubic), as opposed to a ruby crystal (hexagonal).

Spinel

For centuries red spinels were mistaken for rubies, for Europeans saw few uncut crystals in the lots brought by traders from the East. Eventually

46

chemists discovered that spinel, unlike corundum, contains a large amount of magnesium in its chemical composition and that it forms cubic instead of hexagonal crystals. Clearly it was a separate and, apparently, a commoner mineral. Sadly enough, most of the important old "rubies" turned out to be spinels.

Imperial State Crown includes the red spinel known as the Black Prince "Ruby."

47

Even after spinel was identified, red stones often were called "balas rubies," and to some gem merchants they are still known by this name.

Spinel also is found in Ceylon, Burma and Siam, for it seems to grow in the same way, in the same rocks, as the corundum gems. Red is only one of its colors. Others are deep blue, black, brown-orange, pink and mauve. Spinel has only slightly less refraction (1.72) than corundum, but often is duller and darker than it should be, for most spinels are badly cut, a result of trying to get too big a stone for the depth of the rough.

Red spinels also can be mistaken for pyrope (from the Greek *pyr*: fire) garnets. Both stones have a hardness of about 8, both have high single refraction, and both crystallize in the cubic group of crystals. One way to tell the difference between these two gemstones is by their *specific gravity*. This is how much a mineral weighs compared to an equal volume of water. Red spinel has a specific gravity of 3.6, which means it is 3.6 times as heavy as water. Pyrope garnet has a specific gravity of 3.5. The specific gravity of most minerals is between 2.0 and 4.0, though that of gold is 19.3.

So, next time you see a lovely red jewel that you know must be real, look thrice—it may be a ruby, a spinel or a garnet.

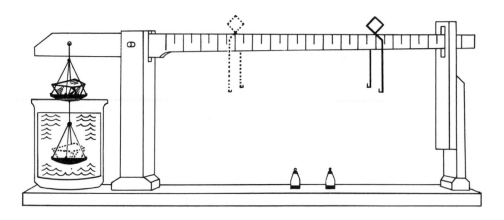

Method of determining specific gravity of stones.
Stones are weighed twice, first in air, and then in water. If we subtract the weight in water from that in air, we find how much the water weighs. That figure, divided into the air weight, gives the specific gravity of the stone.

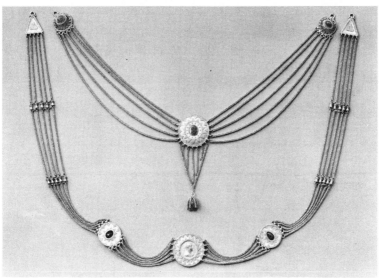

Cleopatra's jewels—her scarabs and beads.

6. Emerald and Aquamarine

CLEOPATRA'S JEWEL BOX must have been filled with emeralds. For the beautiful Egyptian Queen owned the fabled mines which were then a rich source of this gemstone. Cleopatra's mines still exist. Fifty years ago, French fortune hunters explored their tunnels, but in vain. The mines long since had been emptied of gemstones. But in art museum collections you can still see scarabs and beads that are cut from emeralds dug from Cleopatra's mines two thousand years ago. Perhaps, recut and modernized, Cleopatra's own emeralds still exist somewhere.

After ruby, emerald is the rarest and most valued gemstone. And oddly enough, the same chemical impurity which makes corundum a ruby makes an emerald of common beryl.

That a slight amount of chromium oxide should turn one mineral red and another green is one of nature's wonders. What happens is that chromium intermingled with differently spaced corundum and beryl atoms absorbs different wave lengths of light. On the corundum spacing, the green waves are absorbed and not the red; beryl atoms absorb most of the red and not the green. The color you see in the gemstone is, so to speak, the left-over wave length.

Nero's Sun Glasses

Emeralds are so soothing to look at that it is said ancient Roman lapidaries kept them on their worktables to rest their eyes. The Roman emperor, Nero, is supposed to have watched the gladiator contests in the Colosseum through emerald glasses. If the story were true, Nero's lenses could be considered the world's first sun-glasses!

But it is unlikely that even the powerful Nero could have obtained flawless emeralds large enough to use as glasses. You seldom see an emerald of any size without a flaw. And most emeralds are small, although other beryl crystals sometimes grow very large. One such beryl crystal, found in a pegmatite dike in Maine, was 20 feet long and weighed several tons!

This huge crystal was too flawed to be cut into gemstones. But it was still valuable. Beryl is a compound of aluminum, silicon, oxygen and beryllium, a strong, light metal that is widely used in industry. So the Maine deposit was mined for its valuable beryllium.

Beryl crystals are hexagonal, and they usually are found in a coarse sort of granite, in what are called pegmatite dikes, such at the one in Maine. Occasionally, beryl crystals form in veins—gases carry the beryllium from slowly cooling molten rock and deposit it along the crevices of an overlying bed. In some places, these vein crystals are emeralds.

The Inca Emeralds

Today's finest emeralds come from the jungles of Colombia. The famous mines at Muzo have been producing rich green stones since the days when the Incas ruled over this part of South America.

Emeralds were hardly known in Europe before Francisco Pizarro and a handful of Spanish soldiers conquered the fabulous Inca empire in the 16th century. The Spanish soldiers, unsure what the Inca's lovely green jewels were, put the stones to an ancient test. They struck them with their swords. But the test had been meant for diamonds, the world's hardest substance. Emeralds have a hardness of only 8, and their flaws make them even more brittle. So many magnificent Inca emeralds were shattered into fragments!

Later, when the Spaniards discovered the true value of these emeralds, they tried to find the source of the stones. But even under torture, the

Incas would not reveal the location of the mines. It was only by accident that the Muzo mines were discovered in 1558. Many other Inca mines never were found. They are still there, hidden in the hills, waiting for some daring prospector to uncover them.

Emeralds Around the World

Emeralds also are found in Africa, India, Pakistan and the United States. They used to be found in Siberia, near Sverdlovsk. Siberian emeralds are a slightly yellower green than Colombian stones. Many of them are set in the old Russian crown jewels, which the Soviets seized during the Russian Revolution in 1919.

Crabtree Mt., North Carolina, is the site of the only American emerald mine. The tiny green crystals are embedded in a matrix of black and white rock. Large, clear emeralds have been found in nearby Hiddenite in a plowed field. But they are pale inside, so they are worth more as interesting specimens than as cut stones. Payment of a small fee entitles visitors to search for specimens at Crabtree Mt.

Emerald crystal in matrix of white and gray calcite from Muzo, Colombia.

Aquamarine crystal and cut stone from Minas Gerais, Brazil.

Aquamarines

The blue-green variety of beryl is called aquamarine. A tiny amount of scandium, a very rare metal, in the beryl may give aquamarine its color.

Aquamarines usually are found in long hexagonal crystals. They are among nature's most beautiful crystals, and they often grow very large. In the American Museum of Natural History in New York you can see a fine 20-pound blue aquamarine. It was broken off with a sledge hammer from a 273-pound crystal!

The largest aquamarines are not always the most valuable. Deep blue aquamarines make the most beautiful jewels, and deep color is rarer in a 5-carat stone than in a 50-carat one. So by the carat the most costly aquamarines are deeply colored 4- to 8-carat stones.

Even a 5-carat aquamarine looks fairly large. It is about a third larger than, say, a 5-carat sapphire. That's because corundum has a specific gravity of 4.0 and beryl has a specific gravity of only 2.6. So in corundum weight is packed into a smaller space than it is in beryl, making a sapphire smaller than an aquamarine of equal weight.

Brazil is the most important source of aquamarines. The supply of fine stones, however, is much smaller than it used to be. The tropical island of Madagascar is the second most important source of these stones. A

53

lovely, though small, blue aquamarine is found in Southwest Africa, and a few stones come from Mozambique, India, Ceylon and the United States.

Aquamarine often has a greenish tint. The green can be eliminated by carefully heating the stone. The less than red hot heat removes the yellow from the green (green is a combination of blue and yellow), leaving a purer blue color. Brazilian gem merchants have already done this with most of the aquamarines that are shipped to the United States.

Golden Beryl

Some of the yellow gemstones you see are beryls. They are called golden beryls. The best are a deep golden color; less valuable are the light yellow stones and the pale greenish-yellow beryls called heliodor ("sun's gift"). Golden beryls are found in Southwest Africa. When they are heated, they turn to pale blue aquamarines.

Morganite

In 1911, a pink beryl was discovered in California. It was named morganite, in honor of financier J. P. Morgan, who donated the start of its gem collection to New York's American Museum of Natural History. The California specimens of morganite turned out to be too pale to make good gems, but at about the same time a deep pink morganite that makes a handsome gemstone was found in Madagascar.

Collector's Item

An unusual aquamarine is found in Brazil and Mozambique. If you view it from one angle, the stone looks almost black; but from another angle it looks pale blue. Tiny inclusions which lie in dense but paper-thin layers parallel to the base of the crystal cause the difference. Seen from the top, the inclusions make the stone completely opaque, but the crystal becomes transparent when viewed from the side. These aquamarines are cut en cabochon. You can see a weak star on the dome of the cabochon, a star which resembles the star in Australian black star sapphires.

Alexandrite crystal and cut stone.

7. Alexandrite and Cat's-eyes

APRIL 29, 1839 BEGAN like any other day for the miners of Ekaterinburg, a small Russian town in the great Ural mountains. The men woke up and ate an early breakfast. Then they went to their jobs in the nearby emerald mines.

But that day, as the miners dug along the walls of the pegmatite, looking for emeralds, they found some unusual green crystals. These crystals were flatter than emerald crystals, and they had small notches in each edge.

That night the miners told their friends about the strange green crystals they had found. "Here are a few," said one miner, pulling some stones from his pocket and moving closer to the lamplight.

"But these stones are red, not green," someone observed. And so they were.

The miners were amazed. "They were green this morning!" they insisted.

"Let us wait until morning and see if they turn green again," one of the men suggested.

That is what they did. And the next morning, the stones were green again.

Alexander's Birthday Gift

The miners' discovery soon became the world's most fascinating gemstone. It was named alexandrite, after the Crown Prince of Russia, Count Alexander Nicolaivich, later Czar Alexander II. The discovery had been made on his 21st birthday.

Later, scientists determined that the change of color in alexandrite is due to the kind of light in which you look at the stone. If you see it in ordinary daylight it is bluish-green. The same stone seen in artificial light is purplish-red.

Why? You will recall that light is made up of every color in the rainbow, and that different minerals absorb different colors. Alexandrite absorbs all the colors of light except red and part of the blue and green. So blue and green, which are stronger than red in daylight, give alexandrite its daytime color. And red, which is stronger than blue and green in the light from a lantern or electric bulb, gives the stone its evening color.

You may have heard that painters prefer to paint in "north light." That's because blues and greens are stronger in north light, and the colors of objects stand out more sharply. For the same reason, gem merchants prefer to examine jewels in north light.

Alexandrites are even rarer than rubies or emeralds, gem quality stones being found only in Russia and Ceylon. Indeed, today you pay more for a good alexandrite than for a fair emerald. Russian alexandrites are small and usually flawed. But there is more blue in their green and more purple in their red than there is in the Ceylonese stones. Ceylonese alexandrites are a yellowish green by daylight, a brownish red by electric light. Many Ceylon stones are flawless and may weigh as much as fifty carats.

Chrysoberyl

Alexandrite is really an unusual kind of chrysoberyl, a mineral composed of aluminum, oxygen and beryllium. Ordinary chrysoberyl, which also can be a gemstone, is greenish yellow to greenish brown. A tiny iron impurity probably gives it its color. (Alexandrite, like emerald and ruby, gets its color from a chromium impurity.)

As you might guess from the names, beryl and chrysoberyl have something in common—beryllium! Beryl contains silicon, chrysoberyl does not. Yet chrysoberyl also forms in pegmatites where silicon is available. and no one knows why the two substances do not combine to become beryl. Pressure may be involved, for chrysoberyl crystals never are found in open gem pockets as beryl crystals sometimes are.

Chrysoberyl crystallizes in an orthorhombic pattern. Crystals often grow together in twos (twins) or threes (trillings), with a result that looks like the spokes of a wheel. Often the crystals are translucent rather than transparent. Clear crystals are sometimes cut into brilliants, for chrysoberyl has strong (1.75) refraction and, softer only than diamond and corundum, is the third hardest gemstone. Chrysoberyl's hardness is 8½—harder than beryl but not so hard as corundum.

The best chrysoberyls come from Minas Novas, Brazil. Of these, the loveliest are the brilliant chartreuse-yellow stones. You can see a 75-carat emerald-cut one at the American Museum of Natural History in New York. It is one of the largest clear chrysoberyls ever cut.

Cat's-eyes

Chrysoberyl with tiny needle-like inclusions lying in a parallel pattern are called cat's-eyes. Like alexandrites, cat's-eyes are expensive stones.

You see cat's-eye gemstones in the same colors as real cats' eyes—from yellow-green to fairly dark brown. The "eye" is nearly white in pale stones, bluish in dark ones. As in star stones, there must be just enough needles in a cat's-eye to make the pattern look as though it is inside the stone and not on the surface.

When a gemmologist speaks of cat's-eyes, he generally means the chrysoberyl cat's-eye that are found in Ceylon and Brazil. But there are other cat's-eyes stones, too. You see aquamarine, morganite and golden beryl cat's-eyes. These come from Brazil, except for golden beryl cat's-eyes, which, so far, have been found only in Madagascar.

All cat's-eyes, like star stones, are known as "phenomenal" stones and are cut en cabochon.

Andalusite

Andalusite, a gemstone often called "the poor man's alexandrite," also appears to change color, but for a different reason than alexandrite. Andalusite crystals are strongly *pleochroic*—they absorb different colors when viewed from different angles. If you see andalusite from the side, it looks green; from the ends, it looks reddish-brown.

Chiastolite, an unusual variety of andalusite, shows a black and white Maltese cross when its long, cigar-shaped crystal is sliced. The black areas are solid inclusions which were pushed together by the chiastolite atoms as the crystal formed. Chiastolite gets its name from the Greek letter *chi*, which has a shape like our X.

Like chrysoberyl, andalusite crystallizes in an orthorhombic pattern. But, unlike chrysoberyl, its crystals do not grow together in twos and threes. Andalusite has a hardness of only 7½ and a medium (1.63) refraction.

Although andalusite gemstones now come mainly from Brazil, the mineral gets its name from the original non-gemmy deposit in Andalusia, Spain. The names of all recently discovered minerals end in *ite* (from the Greek *ith* or *lith*: stone). The stem of the mineral's name may refer to a place (andalusite), a person (morganite), or the mineral's chemical composition and/or a property (phosphophyllite—a phosphate that breaks into leafy scales).

Peridot, the most ancient of gem stones. Often called "evening emerald" because of its more intense green by artificial light.

8. Peridot and Topaz

WHAT AN EXCITING GEMSTONE peridot is. It is mined by ants and rains down upon men from outer space. In ancient Rome it was known as topaz, and today it is popularly called the "evening emerald."

According to Pliny, a first century Roman naturalist, there was a special glowing topaz on Chitis, a mysterious fog-bound island in the Red Sea. The fog-shrouded island is still there, just opposite the Red Sea port of Berenice. Now it is called Zebirget, or St. John's Island. But the gemstone found there is peridot, not topaz.

The greenish-yellow peridot doesn't remotely resemble our topaz. But peridot must be the stone Pliny called topaz because he wrote that Chitis topaz, unlike other topaz, could be polished with an iron file. Iron will not scratch true topaz, which has a hardness of 8, but it will scratch peridot, which has a hardness of 6½ to 7.

Ant Hills and Outer Space

Peridot is a kind of olivine, one of the important minerals in common lava. So you find this gemstone near volcanic rocks, as in some of the rocks and craters of Arizona and New Mexico.

It is in these deposits in the Southwest that ants mine peridots. The tiny peridot pebbles, which withstand weathering better than the surrounding rock, are scattered throughout the soil of the area. As the ants tunnel through this earth, the pebbles block their way. The ants push the pebbles out onto a waste pile—the ant hill—where anyone can pick them up.

But these peridots are small and so abundant that they are practically valueless. The larger peridots come from St. John's Island and Burma.

Well-formed peridot crystal from St. John's Island in the Red Sea.

A French company used to mine the stones of the island every few years. The company chartered a steamship, loaded it with miners and supplies, and steamed off to the island. When the supplies ran out, the expedition returned to France and the company sold off the peridots, a few at a time.

Peridot crystals are orthorhombic and have strong double refraction which makes them look slightly fuzzy inside. The name "the evening emerald" comes from the fact that peridot's yellow-green color seems greener under artificial light.

Peridot sometimes is found in meteorites—masses of stone or metal which crash into the earth from outer space. It is our only crystallized gemstone from outer space!

Most meteorites are small, and they burn up in the earth's atmosphere before reaching the ground, but a few fall to earth. Large meteorites explode when they strike the ground, leaving deep craters. In Arizona, near Flagstaff, you can see a meteorite crater 4,000 feet across and 600 feet deep!

There are three types of meteorites: the irons, the stony irons, and the stones. One kind of stony iron called pallasite has coarse peridot crystals scattered through it so that a slab looks like a slice of fruit cake. A few of these peridots have been cut into small gemstones. Imagine wearing a ring with a stone that has travelled for billions of years in outer space!

True Topaz

Peridot no longer is mistaken for topaz. But to the layman there still is some confusion about what is or is not topaz. What jewelers call "topaz" is actually the brown variety of quartz which gemmologists call citrine.

Jewelers give the name "precious topaz" to true golden-brown vein topaz, and it is much more costly than quartz. True topaz also is found in pink and pale blue tints. You have to look closely to tell the difference between a blue topaz and a pale aquamarine. Without a test even an expert can be fooled. When blue topaz was first discovered in Brazil, American gem buyers thought the new stone was a pale aquamarine, an expensive mistake because aquamarine is more costly than topaz.

You can change brown vein topaz to pink by heating it carefully. A century ago pink topaz was considered more valuable than the brown variety, so the brown stones were heated. Now the brown color is considered equally valuable. But if you ever see a colorless museum specimen labeled, "TOPAZ, SHERRY BROWN," don't be surprised. Brown pegmatite topaz loses its color on long exposure to light, and may even turn blue.

A giant, 600-pound, colorless topaz crystal from Brazil, admired by Herbert P. Whitlock, Wayne Faunce and the author, on its installation in the Morgan Hall of the American Museum of Natural History.

Three common elements, aluminum, silicon and oxygen, plus one rare one, fluorine, make up topaz. Fluorine, a gas, is the substance used in "fluoridating" the drinking water of many cities. Topaz forms in pegmatites and in veins. It crystallizes into an orthorhombic pattern, but the pegmatite crystals look different from the vein crystals.

Most topaz comes from pegmatites, where the crystals are usually large and colorless, light brown, or blue. In the American Museum of Natural History in New York you can see a 600 pound colorless topaz. It is the largest topaz ever found.

Golden-brown topaz, however, is found only in veins, and the crystals are long and slender. These veins are formed by fluorine gas

"Precious" topaz crystals from Brazil. They tend to be more elongated than the colorless or blue pegmatite crystals.

escaping from slowly cooling magma. The gas seeps up through cracks in the rocks of the outer crust and reacts with their minerals. The most important vein deposits of topaz are near Ouro Preto in Brazil.

Topazes have enough refraction (1.62) to make attractive brilliants. They also cleave easily across the long face of the crystals, a fact which lapidaries must take into account when they cut the rough stones into gem size. Usually they are cut in elongated shapes, since the crystals have that shape and bigger stones will result.

64

9. Garnets

IT IS SAID THAT the only light in Noah's Ark was a huge red garnet. What a curious light it must have been! But, then, garnet is a curious stone. It is not a single mineral but a group of minerals with similar chemical compositions and slightly different properties. You will find only one property common to all garnets: cubic system crystals with, of course, single refraction.

Garnets are found in many kinds of rocks all over the world. The garnet minerals fall into six general types. These are: pyrope, almandine, grossular, spessartine, uvarovite and andradite. You may think of garnets as red stones, and many are. But they can also be green, orange, purple, brown or black.

COURTESY OF B. M. SCHAUB

Typical garnet crystal embedded in matrix.

Pyropes of a Past Age

Most of the garnets you see in jewelry are deep, yellow-red pyropes. Sometimes they are mistaken for rubies or spinels. In fact, pyropes found in Kimberley, South Africa, are locally called "Cape rubies."

Pyropes form mainly in volcanic rocks. Arizona anthills may be strewn with pyropes as well as peridots, and small, but flawless, pyropes are found in Bohemia. A century ago, brooches, bracelets and rings were studded with tiny Bohemian garnets. Three thousand Bohemian lapidaries were kept busy cutting garnet gemstones. But the gem-studded Victorian jewelry (so named after England's Queen Victoria, who reigned from 1837 to 1901) no longer is so fashionable, and the garnet industry in Bohemia employs only a few lapidaries now.

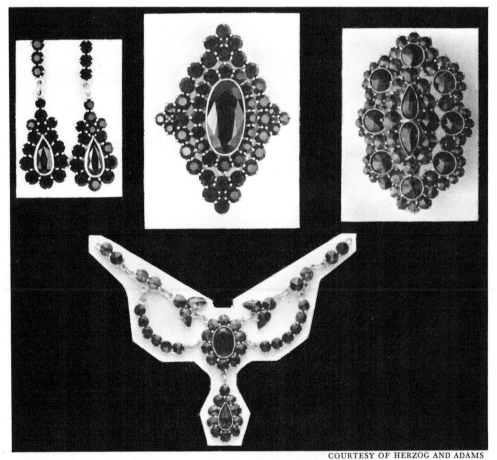

COURTESY OF HERZOG AND ADAMS

Bohemian garnet jewelry of the Victorian era.

66

Large pyropes still are valuable, but they are rare. Pyrope crystals even the size of a pea are uncommon, and you will see very few as large as a hazelnut.

Giant garnet crystals rimmed with black hornblende. Mined in New York State's Adirondack mountains.

Almandine Carbuncles and Sandpaper

Violet-red almandine garnets are found in India, Ceylon and Madagascar. Those from Ceylon and Madagascar are clear and are cut into brilliants. But most Indian almandines have microscopic inclusions of the mineral hornblende in the crystals. Some of the stones even show weak 4-rayed star patterns when Indian almandines are cut en cabochon. These famous "carbuncles" are a deep violet-red—so deep that often the back of the stone is hollowed out to lighten the color.

You can visit a large almandine garnet mine much closer to home, on Gore Mountain at North Creek, New York, where garnet crystals are embedded in rock and rimmed with black hornblende. Some of the crystals are as large as three feet across. Unfortunately, they have been so cracked and flawed by the pressure of the inclosing rock that only

67

small pieces can be cut as gemstones. But they are valuable as the "sand" in garnet sandpaper.

Garnet is harder than quartz, the usual stone used in sandpaper, and it breaks into sharper-edged fragments. It also is slightly magnetic, so the sandpaper manufacturer puts a strong magnet below the paper, drawing the garnet to the wet glue. The garnet fragments, with the sharp cutting edges pointing upward, settle on the paper.

An unusual pyrope-almandine garnet is found in North Carolina. It is called rhodolite because its pale red-violet color resembles the hue of the mountain rhododendron. Rhodolite has a hardness of 7½ and high (1.75) refraction, but only small stones can be cut from the crystals. Larger ones have recently been found in Tanzania, from which deposit one stone of over 100 carats has been cut.

"Cinnamon" and "Jade" Grossular

One of the loveliest garnets is an orange-brown stone found in Ceylon. It is a variety of grossular called hessonite, sometimes referred to as "cinnamon stone" because it is the color of the bark of a cinnamon tree. Unfortunately, hessonite chips rather easily and you seldom see an undamaged cut stone.

Grossular is found in light green and pale pink tints, too. A finely crystalline, compact light green grossular from Pretoria, in the Transvaal, is called "South African Jade." It is found in translucent veins speckled or streaked with a black chromium ore called chromite. South African Jade, its green spotted here and there with black, makes attractive cabochons, ashtrays and carvings.

Once-rare Spessartine

Spessartine is a brownish red garnet which was a rare gemstone until a large deposit was discovered in Poços de Cavallos, Brazil. You see two kinds of Cavallos spessartines, neither very satisfactory. One is lightly colored but badly flawed; the other is only slightly flawed but dark brown.

The best spessartines come from an old deposit near Fortaleza, Brazil. Its crystals are small but completely clear and nicely colored, and they make handsome gems. You can see what may be the largest Fortaleza

68

spessartine, a 5-carat stone, in New York's American Museum of Natural History.

Uvarovite, the Uncut Gemstone

Uvarovite is a magnificent deep emerald-green chromium garnet. But no crystal both large enough and clear enough to cut ever has been found, so uvarovite remains merely an interesting (and expensive) mineral specimen.

The Unique Andradite

The rarest and most valuable garnet is the emerald-green demantoid variety of andradite. Unfortunately, the only good source of this garnet, an alluvial gold mine in the Ural Mountains near what was, in Czarist days, Nizhni-Tagilsk, no longer produces gold nor any stones. So any demantoids you see probably come from antique jewelry.

Demantoids are small but they have high (1.88) refraction and dispersion, which gives them great fire and brilliance. A fine 5-carat demantoid is more beautiful than many emeralds, and very much rarer.

For some unknown reason, jewelers call demantoid "olivine," which is the mineral name of peridot. It is the only instance in which jewelers have reversed their usual practice, and call an expensive stone by the name of a less expensive one.

10. Jade

CHINESE JADE CARVINGS ARE FAMOUS throughout the world for their exquisite delicacy and detailed craftsmanship. You must have seen examples of fine jade carvings in your wanderings through museums, or in shops selling antiques and oriental wares. The Chinese have crafted jade into lamp bases, cups, plates and decorative figurines. The inscrutable smooth, translucent jade figures often seem to hold all the secrets of the Orient.

But curiously enough, little or none of the jade that is carved in China is found there. The rough stones come from Burma, Turkestan, Tibet and New Zealand. Before World War II, the Chinese bought jade even from Wyoming!

You will recall that the word "jade" comes from the Spanish *piedra de ijada,* "stone of the side." Actually, the jade you see in carvings and jewels is either of two minerals, nephrite and jadeite.

Nephrite or "Spinach" Jade

Nephrite is one of a group of chemically similar minerals called amphiboles (from the Greek *amphibolos*: of uncertain or many-sided nature). Its typical color is spinach-green, but nephrite is found also in white, blue, yellow and black. The colors usually are dull, so nephrite is more popular for large carvings than for small jewelry.

Many of the ancient Chinese carvings of animals you see in museum collections are nephrite. They were used in burial ceremonies as long as 3,000 years ago. The very oldest carvings often are brown or dull red, the surface color of the jade having been changed from its original green by centuries of weathering in the soil.

Nephrite looks slightly different from jadeite, even when the colors of the two stones are almost the same. Jadeite crystals are coarser and stubbier than those of nephrite, and jadeite's hues are brighter. You can see the difference in crystals between the two stones under a microscope. Even more marked is the difference in specific gravity—2.9 to 3.0 for nephrite, 3.3 for jadeite.

Serpentine, sometimes called "Soochow jade," looks like nephrite but is much softer and can be scratched by a knife. Like nephrite,

Ming dynasty wine pot decorated with a rare form of "Shou" mark in opaque white nephrite jade.

71

it makes graceful carvings, but it is very much less costly and is more easily broken.

Jadeite, the Gem of the Orient

The emerald-green color which is characteristic of the most beautiful jade is found only in jadeite. The finest jadeite is translucent as well. Most of it comes from Burma.

Jadeite is one of a group of chemically similar minerals called pyroxenes, a word of Greek origin which means "stranger to fire." Ancient mineralogists mistakenly thought pyroxenes would not be found in igneous rocks.

You seldom see a large piece of emerald-green jadeite. The emerald-green color usually is concentrated in a small area of a large boulder of jadeite which contains many hues of green. The skilled jade carver, working with such a block of jadeite, uses the spot of emerald green to highlight a flower or a bird in his carving.

Jadeite is found in some of the same colors as nephrite, and also in red-browns, mustard-yellow, orange-browns and pale blues or mauves. You sometimes hear of "pink" jade; this is really a pale lilac-colored or "mauve" jadeite.

"Educated Feet" and "Finger Stones"

Jade is found in boulders in stream beds or former river channels. Natives with "educated feet' wade through streams in Burma looking for jadeite masses. Jadeite, because of its coarse crystals, weathers with a distinctive, granular surface. The natives can often identify a jadeite boulder simply by stepping on it!

Jade is a soft stone but difficult to break. That sounds contradictory, but it isn't. The crystals of the jade minerals are tiny grains which interlock in all directions. This makes the stone difficult to break because no cleavage can continue for more than a fraction of an inch, the length of a separate grain. That's why jade can be carved into delicate patterns without breaking.

Yet nephrite has a hardness of only 5 to 6, and jadeite has a hardness of 6½ to 7. So, although you cannot break jade easily, you can wear

72

it down. In fact, one characteristic of genuine jade is a slightly uneven polished surface. The crystals which are matted together to make jade are softer parallel to their length than they are across it. These softer directions wear down a little faster than the harder ones, leaving a slightly uneven surface.

If you have touched polished jade, you know how smooth and pleasant it feels. Many Chinese carry a "fingering stone" in their pockets—a small piece of jade which they rub to calm their nerves.

The Lost Mexican Jade

The only Mexican jade you are likely to see—and generally only in a museum—was carved centuries ago by the ancient Mayan Indians. Their jade sources have never been found. When the Mayan civilization died, the secret of its jade deposits apparently died with it.

Mexican jade is jadeite, and it is often a brilliant emerald-green. The Mayans valued it more highly than gold, and like the ancient Chinese, they used it in their burial ceremonies. So-called "Mexican jade" which is sold to tourists today is not jade at all, but a soft, banded onyx-marble, dyed green. It can be scratched easily with a knife.

Some scientists have suggested that the discovery of jadeite in Central America indicates that an oriental people migrated there from Asia, bringing the jade with them. But Mexican jadeite has a slightly different chemical composition from that of Burmese jadeite, so the facts do not support the migration theory.

*Egyptian XII dynasty girdle of gold cowries, and amulet of gold, carnelian and
turquoise beads, belonging to Princess Sat-hathor-iunut.*

11. Turquoise, Lapis Lazuli and Feldspars

LIKE JADE, turquoise and lapis lazuli are opaque gemstones. So are the
feldspars, which are better known by their gem names, "moonstone,"
labradorite, and microcline, or "Amazonstone."

Some of these stones have been used in jewelry for thousands of
years. The earliest known jewelry, the bracelets of Queen Zer of the first
Egyptian dynasty, contain alternate pieces of gold and turquoise. And
lapis lazuli has been found in the ruins of ancient Babylonia.

The Desert Gemstone

The word "turquoise" comes from the French *pierre turquoise*,
"stone of Turkey." No turquoises are found in Turkey, but for hundreds

74

of years Istanbul, the capitol of Turkey, was the trading center through which these stones reached Europe from Iran.

The best turquoise still comes from the centuries-old Persian mines near Nishapur. Persian poets compare the turquoise's pure blue color to a cloudless summer sky. Turquoise also is found in Tibet, Egypt, Chile and the American Southwest. The American Indians mined turquoise long before the Spanish conquest, and today it is still the typical stone of Navajo jewelry.

Turquoise forms in veins in weathered, altered rocks. It is a compound of copper, aluminum, phosphorus, oxygen and hydrogen. You will recall that in Chapter 3 turquoise was described as a "secondary" mineral. This is a mineral formed from elements which are dissolved from other minerals in surface rock by weathering and carried into cracks in deeper rocks by seeping water. The elements in this case are copper, which gives turquoise its bright blue color, aluminum and phosphorus.

You might think a heavy flow of water would be needed to wash these elements down into fresh rock. But the places where turquoise is found, except for Tibet, are desert regions where water is scarce. And Tibet is frozen so much of the year that little water flows there.

What accounts for this apparent inconsistency? There are two factors. Dissolved elements concentrate more heavily in a thin trickle of water seeping down through the rocks than they would in a heavy flow.

Turquoise seam cutting rock and necklace of turquoise beads.

75

Also, in a wet climate, the element-laden water hits the water table—the level of water-saturated rocks—after only a few feet. But in a dry climate, the water can seep more deeply (although never very deep) and deposit its elements in the rock crevices as it dries up.

Missing Crystals and Plastic Color

For a long time mineralogists thought that all turquoise, like opal, was very fine-grained, seemingly amorphous—at least without any crystal shape. Then turquoise crystals were discovered in a deposit near Lynch Station, Virginia. These microscopic rhombs in thin crusts are the only known turquoise crystals. However, they are suitable only as specimens; they do not make good gemstones.

Turquoise veins are thin. The brown and black patterns you see in many turquoises are pieces of the neighboring wall rock where the vein is found. It is hard to imitate these mottled turquoises in glass, and for that reason many gem merchants prefer them to the pure sky-blue stones.

Not surprisingly, turquoise contains considerable water in its composition. Many stones seem a rich blue when they are mined, but turn white and crumble when the water dries out. Grease and dirt can soak into turquoise, too, for most turquoise is porous and has a hardness of only 5 to 6.

At one time pale, earthy, dried-out turquoises were soaked in paraffin or oil in an attempt to fill the pores. The oil, in replacing the water, also intensified the stones' color. However, oil-soaked turquoise turns green after a while.

Now liquid plastic is used instead of oil to fill the pores of turquoise. Often a little artificial color is added to the plastic. Much of the turquoise you see now in jewelry is treated this way, and, since most tests are somewhat destructive, even an expert is sometimes fooled.

The Painter's Gemstone

The "sapphire" of Biblical times was lapis lazuli, a soft, violet-blue stone composed of sodium, calcium, aluminum and sulphur. Its mineral name is lazurite, which, like lapis lazuli, means "blue stone."

Lazurite forms cubic system crystals, but you seldom see them. Like turquoise, lazurite usually is found in grainy masses spread through the

Beads of lapis lazuli.

surrounding rock. The blue surface of such lazurite is dotted with golden specks of pyrite, or "fools' gold." In fact, the presence of pyrite in the gemstone is one's assurance that the stone is genuine lapis lazuli.

The next time you see a painting by the great Italian Renaissance painter, Leonardo da Vinci, look at the ultramarines closely. That paint was made from crushed lapis lazuli!

It was an expensive color, as you can imagine. To save money, Renaissance pigment sellers often substituted for the costly lapis lazuli a less expensive blue made from azurite, a common copper mineral. But azurite contains water, and in nature it can form a more stable green mineral, malachite, upon the addition of a little more water. So azurite paint sometimes turns green, after it has been on the canvas or a wall for many years. Should you see a famous Renaissance painting with green where blue should be, you'll know how it got that way, and why.

Today painters do not have this worry. Ultramarine is no longer so costly, for it is produced synthetically.

A medium quality of blue lazurite is found in Chile. This is the lapis lazuli you see in inexpensive "real stone" cuff links and cabochon rings.

It is fairly abundant. Much rarer is the deep violet-blue lazurite, the "sapphire" of Biblical days. It comes from the Badakshan district of Afghanistan, and it is mined just as it was 3,000 years ago.

The Badakshan lazurite is embedded in cliff rock. Natives build fires against the cliffs, then throw cold water on the hot rock. The sudden change of temperature cracks the rock, which the natives then pry off in flat slabs.

No doubt modern mining methods in Afghanistan would produce more fine lapis lazuli in less time. But then these lovely gemstones would not be so rare and their value would fall for a time, till the deposit ran out. Unhurried mining has made the deposit last longer.

The Feldspars

The feldspars are a group of chemically similar compounds which, considered as one substance, make up the world's most abundant mineral. They have a hardness of 6 and are the principal minerals of igneous and plutonic rocks. Three of the feldspars, microcline, albite-oligoclase and labradorite, provide gemstones.

Microcline is found in granite pegmatites in place of orthoclase, the feldspar of common granite. Both orthoclase and microcline are distinct from the plagioclase series of feldspars, minerals which differ only slightly one from the other. Labradorite and a variety of albite-oligoclase called "moonstone" are plagioclases.

Labradorite

There is a Brazilian butterfly whose wings reflect a brilliant blue when they are seen from certain angles, but when seen from straight above reflect no blue at all. The color is caused by tiny transparent overlapping scales which affect light so that they absorb certain wave lengths. Labradorite is, in effect, very similar to this butterfly. Small plates of a closely related feldspar lie in fixed planes inside labradorite. These regular inclusions cause the stone to give off a brilliantly colored blue reflection as it is turned to the proper angle.

The lapidary must be careful to cut labradorite cabochons so that the *labradorescence*, as this effect is called, shows on the stone's face.

78

Labradorite, as you would guess, comes from the peninsula of Labrador, although a labradorite used to decorate buildings comes from Norway. You can see slabs of this polished stone with its shiny blue grains on the facade of the Chrysler Building in New York. The finest gemstones come from Finland.

Polished white moonstone with a bluish sheen.

"Moonstone"

The most valuable of the feldspar gemstones is "moonstone," a white, translucent albite-oligoclase mineral with a light-blue sheen. Adularia, a clear white orthoclase found in the central Alps (once called the Adular Mountains), can also show a blue sheen. This effect is known as *adularescence*, and it is much like labradorescence.

The best moonstones come from Ceylon. Cameo cutters look for large flat pieces on which they can carve portraits, but large stones are becoming increasingly rare. A deposit of moonstone discovered recently in India contains gray, greenish and orange stones. When they are cut into high domes—the wrong way to cut moonstone—they often show four-rayed stars.

Microcline

The coarse feldspar of granite pegmatites is chemically the same as the feldspar in normal granite. Since the crystal structure is different it

79

has been called microcline. Most of it is reddish or white. It is used in the making of porcelain glazes and is one of the principal substances for which pegmatites are mined. Mica is another, and the gems, like beryl and topaz, may be only by-products.

Amazonstone, named long ago because it was found in the possession of Brazilian Indians, is a green variety of microcline. It is fairly common and makes another inexpensive jewelry stone.

St. Edward's Crown

CROWN JEWELS

of England are preserved in the Tower of London and are used at coronations.

St. Edward's crown is made of gold weighing nearly five pounds. It was first made for King Charles II, designed to surmount his long flowing black periwig.

The sceptre contains the Star of Africa, a 530 carat diamond, the largest cut diamond in existence.

Queen's Sceptre

IOPE DIAMOND
The famous 44 ct. blue stone to be seen at the J. S. National Museum in Washington.

DeLONG RUBY
A recent 100 ct. gem star ruby in New York's Museum of Natural History.

AGATE
Too often the banded micro crystalline quartz from Brazil, commonly called agate, is drably colored when it is found. German lapidaries use analine and chemical dyes to emphasize the layered structure and make it a colorful decorative stone. Some bands color better than others and exaggerate the layered arrangement.

CORAL
The ox-blood red skeleton of a marine animal supplies the Japanese artist with a fine raw material. The jeweler uses it for necklaces.

JADE
Many shades and tints characterize this compact and tenacious mineral which lends itself to exquisite carvings and utmost delicacy.

QUARTZ ROCK CRYSTAL
Even though quartz is the commonest of minerals, its clarity, hardness, and colorful variety make the coarsely crystalline types the most widely used stones of the jewelry trade. Amethyst, citrine, rose quartz, smoky quartz, greened amethyst (called peridine), and rock crystal are only phases of a single compound, silicon dioxide.

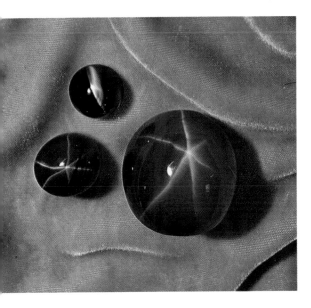

PHENOMENAL STONES
A star ruby, a giant star sapphire and a catseye make this remarkable group of stones with inclusions that reflect light.

EMERALD CRYSTALS
Chromium-greened beryl crystals never grow as large and clear as those without chromium.

TURQUOISE NAVAJO JEWELRY
Only the simplest smoothing brings out turquoise's clear beauty. Hence primitive civilizations the world over have recognized its decorative worth, not needing the sophisticated treatment that clear stones require.

AMBER
Resin from long-buried pine-like trees provides a unique gemstone, a substance so light it drifts away in sea water.

SMOKY QUARTZ AND AMAZONSTONE
Common minerals of granite, but pure enough and large enough, they can appear in jewelry.

DIAMOND IN MATRIX
Luster suggesting that diamonds would stick in grease can be seen even in the photograph.

AMETHYST AND CRYSTALS
Most costly of all quartz varieties, amethyst still poses a problem. Analyses show too little impurity like iron or manganese for either to be responsible alone for its regal hue.

TOPAZ
The various hues displayed by a mineral expected by most jewelry buyers to come only in brown show how few recognize that labelling citrine quartz as topaz is a serious misuse of the proper name for an outstanding gemstone species.

12. Unappreciated Gemstones

TWO OF THE UNAPPRECIATED gemstones in this chapter, tourmaline and zircon, have been used for decoration for centuries. The other three stones, kunzite, benitoite and hiddenite, are relatively recent discoveries. None of these five transparent stones is as well known as it deserves to be.

Tourmaline, the Electric Gemstone

To Amsterdam in 1703 came a strange yellow-green stone from Ceylon which, when heated, drew ashes and dust to it like a magnet. It was called tourmaline, after the Singhalese word for carnelian, *tormalli.*

You can imagine how excited the Dutch were about this mysterious stone. Tourmaline is still fascinating, more than 260 years later. It has a very variable composition with up to a dozen elements in varying amounts and proportions. The one invariable and essentially rare ingredient is an uncommon element, boron, with silica and alumina.

Tourmaline crystals are unusual, too. The long prisms are trigonal-hexagonal, but the faces on each end are different. This lack of symmetry is known as *hemimorphism* (from the Greek *hemi*: half and *morph*: form), and it accounts for tourmaline's magnetic, or electrical, properties.

Tourmaline's electrical properties make it valuable in industry where it is used in pressure gauges. The different ends of the crystal acquire

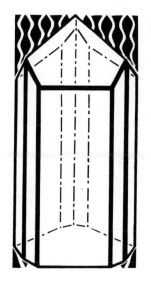

Hemimorphism,
the lack of symmetry
in tourmaline crystals.

positive and negative electrical charges as the prism expands or contracts from heat or pressure. This is what was noticed in Amsterdam in 1703.

Singhalese tourmalines are dull, and they are mostly yellow-green and brown. But in 1820 two boys made a once-in-a-lifetime discovery—a gem pocket on Mt. Mica, near Paris, Maine, containing bright, clear green, red and blue tourmalines! This was developed into a mine. When the supply of Maine stones dwindled, more abundant tourmalines were discovered in California. Many were sent to China for carving. Today, our best tourmalines come from Brazil, Madagascar and Mozambique.

Tourmaline has a hardness of 7 and an index of refraction around 1.63, which makes it suitable for cutting into brilliants as well as emerald cuts. The gemstone colors have been given special names. Red is known

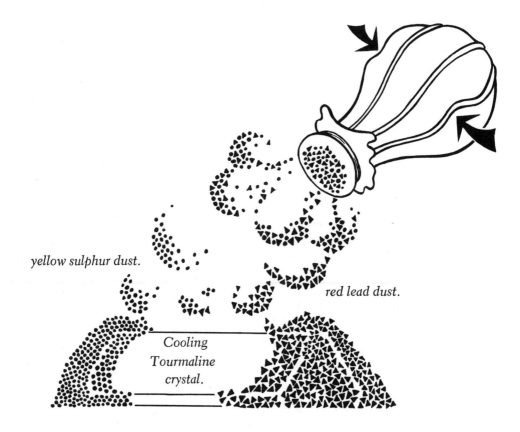

yellow sulphur dust.

red lead dust.

Cooling
Tourmaline
crystal.

As its temperature changes, Tourmaline attracts negative and positive charged particles of red lead and sulphur puffed through a silk screen.

as rubellite and blue is called indicolite. Pure dark green tourmaline is known simply as tourmaline, but seen from the end it looks black. Some tourmaline crystals contain more than one color. "Watermelon" tourmaline is pink in the center and green on the surface.

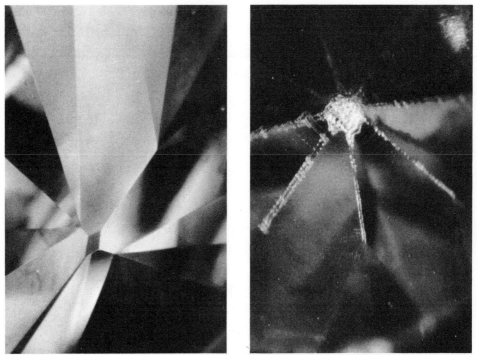

Similarity and dissimilarity of diamond and zircon. A doubling of the back facet edges of the zircon, reveal which is which.

Zircon, the Forgotten Gemstone

Zircon was a charming, inexpensive yellow-brown stone from Ceylon until someone discovered that a near worthless, dark, red-brown variety from Siam could be made blue or colorless by heating. Then zircon suddenly became an inexpensive substitute for diamond.

There is no similarity between the two stones chemically. Diamond is 100% carbon; zircon is a compound of silicon, oxygen and zirconium, a rare metal. The crystals of the two stones, however, are remotely similar,

83

for both are four-sided, though zircons are stretched out, tetragonal. Natural bluish-brown zircon crystals have been found in marble deposits in Sparta, New Jersey and Natural Bridge, New York. All the gemmy examples are from gravels, but they may have weathered from a marble.

To some, zircon seemed to be a good substitute for diamond. Like diamond, zircon has great fire and sparkle, the result of high (1.79 to 1.98) refraction. But zircon has a hardness of only 6½ to 7½, so cut stones soon begin to show signs of wear—nicks along the facet edges. Jewelers also discovered that sunlight shining in show windows turned some of the heated blue zircons back to brown!

So zircon, as a substitute for diamond, promptly went out of fashion. But it is still a charming, inexpensive, brilliant golden brown (and red, orange, green or blue) stone.

Kunzite

Kunzite is the transparent lilac-colored variety of the mineral spodumene, a compound of aluminum, silicon, oxygen and lithium, the world's lightest metal. This lovely gemstone was discovered in 1903 in Pala, California and named after George F. Kunz, gem expert for the famous jewelry firm, Tiffany & Company.

Opaque white spodumene crystals 40 feet long have been found in the Black Hills of South Dakota, but the clear kunzite crystals are seldom more than a foot long—and usually much shorter. The crystals are elongated, flat and monoclinic, with their faces slightly pitted. Although kunzite has since been discovered in some abundance in Brazil and Madagascar, the California stones are the equals of any for gemstones and are more complete as crystals.

Kunzite crystals are very pleochroic, showing a rich pink color in one direction and a paler pink one in another. The lapidary has to take this into consideration when he cuts a stone. But all the pink hues fade somewhat on exposure to light. So kunzite is usually cut into large stones, 10 carats or more, to make as richly hued a gemstone as possible.

Kunzite has a hardness of 7, but it is a much more fragile stone than, say, tourmaline, which also has a hardness of 7. The difference is that kunzite cleaves easily and tourmaline does not.

Hiddenite

In 1879, William E. Hidden, a mineral dealer, while looking for emeralds, discovered emerald-green spodumene crystals in North Carolina. The gemstone, and later the town where it was first discovered, were named Hiddenite.

Since then, green spodumene has been found in Brazil, too, in paler, but bigger pieces. Unfortunately, the largest true North Carolina hiddenites weigh only a few carats, and these are so few you are not likely to see them except in the most complete gem collections.

Benitoite

One of the world's rarest gemstones was first found in America. It is called benitoite, after the only locality where gemmy crystals are found, San Benito County in California.

Blue, triangular benitoite and black prismatic eptunite crystals on matrix.

This blue gemstone is so rare because two of its elements, titanium and barium, seldom have a chance to combine chemically. The California benitoite deposit is in a seam of serpentine, a dark greenish rock, with two other rare titanium minerals, joaquinite and neptunite.

Benitoite is the only mineral that forms trigonal-hexagonal system crystals in which the top and bottom faces are paired. It also has high refraction and strong dispersion. You would think such a unique stone would be one of the world's most valuable jewels. But it has a hardness of only 6 to 6½, and there is little demand for it because benitoite is so rare that most people have never even heard of it.

13. Quartz

QUARTZ IS THE MOST COMMON single mineral on earth, but it also is an important gemstone. You see it all around you on the beach, for most sand is finely ground quartz. The next time you go to the seashore, scoop up a handful of sand and examine it closely. You will see the same quartz which, when the right size and color, makes some of the loveliest gemstones.

Quartz is found almost everywhere in many different forms, but the gemstones can be divided into two types—coarsely crystallized and microcrystalline ("micro" comes from the Greek *mikros*: small). All quartz has a hardness of 7.

Coarsely Crystallized Quartz

Coarsely crystallized quartz is usually transparent; it may be colorless or brightly colored and a single crystal is large enough to cut into a clear stone. Micro-crystalline quartz, on the other hand, cannot be really clear, for it consists of fine-grained masses of microscopic crystals.

There are six color varieties of coarsely crystallized quartz gemstones. These are: rock crystal, smoky quartz, amethyst, citrine, peridine and rose quartz. They form in veins, seams, or pockets of rock, often in well-defined crystals.

Rock Crystal

You won't see many rock crystal jewelry stones. This colorless quartz, which is found in huge crystals, was once important for carving figures, church altar pieces, goblets and platters. Its commonest use in jewelry is in beads for necklaces; it is too weakly refracting to make a brilliant-cut stone.

Fortune tellers' crystal balls used to be ground from rock crystal. Today most "crystal" balls are glass because glass is easy to melt and mold. But if you see a fortune teller with a crystal ball and you want to find out whether the ball is crystal or glass, make a test for double refraction (see Chapter 4) by looking through it. Crystal is doubly refracting and glass is not.

Rock crystal is really more important in industry than as a gemstone. If it were not for "crystals"— thinly sliced pure quartz—you might get

Carved rock-crystal, gold and enamel (Milan, Italy 1570-1600).

three or four radio programs simultaneously every time you tuned in a station. The thin crystals vibrate in an electrically oscillating (vibration) system at a fixed rate, keeping radio transmitters on their own assigned wave-lengths. The telephone company uses these crystals, too, in its extensive electronic equipment.

Synthetic (man-made) quartz crystal.

Less than 10% of the rock crystal which is mined is pure enough to be used in industry. Most rock crystal comes from Brazil and Madagascar, but you will find rock crystal specimen localities near Hot Springs, Arkansas—or in Fonda or Little Falls, New York. It is grown synthetically for the telephone company's use.

Smoky Quartz

Rock crystal with a smoky color is called smoky quartz. Scientists think the color is caused by two factors. One is an aluminum impurity in the rock crystal. The other is natural irradiation of the rock crystal by radioactive minerals. X-rays will turn most rock crystal smoky—the more aluminum in the crystal, the smokier it will turn. But some rock crystal does not darken at all, perhaps because it is very pure and has no aluminum in it.

Amethyst

In Greek legend, a maiden named Amethyst was walking in the forest when she was set upon by the hounds of Bacchus, the god of wine. As Amethyst fled she called for help from the goddess Diana, who changed the maiden into a marble statue. Bacchus, who was sorry about the whole episode, then poured wine on the marble figure, staining it a lovely purple hue.

Amethyst is the most valuable of the quartz gemstones. It is found in Canada, Mexico and many parts of the United States—Maine, Pennsylvania, North Carolina, Arizona and Montana. But Brazil is the main source of gem-quality amethysts.

The best amethysts are "Siberian" stones, which originally came from the Ural Mountains near Ekaterinburg. The mines there no longer produce amethysts, but occasionally a stone with the typical rich red-purple color of a Siberian amethyst comes from one of the other sources.

You might say that the eruption of a volcano is a first step in the formation of many amethysts. Volcanic rock contains dissolved gases. Some dissolved gases escape at the mouth of the volcano; the rest continue to separate from the lava as it flows across the earth. This gas forms bubbles much like the bubbles in spilled soda water spreading across a table top. As the lava cools, the bubbles become round holes in the rock. Later a crust of pointed amethyst crystals may form a lining of these holes.

90

An amethyst found in Pennsylvania.

Such hollow, crystal-lined *geodes* of hard quartz resist weathering longer than the surrounding lava.

Most dark-hued flawless Brazilian amethyst crystals are small, although the original Siberian crystals must have been fairly large, judging from the cut stones. All amethyst crystals are "twinned"—intimately inter-grown in a complex pattern. Sometimes you can see the twinning even in a polished stone, a fingerprint-like marks on a face.

This twinning, in conjunction with an iron impurity and irradiation from naturally radioactive substances, may have something to do with the amethyst's color. But nobody is really sure. It is a mystery that future gemmologists may solve.

LEFT *Amethyst crystal from Bahia, Brazil, showing thumbprint markings.*
RIGHT *Water-worn natural citrine crystal point.*

Citrine

Some time ago, probably by accident, miners discovered that most Brazilian amethysts, when heated, turned a golden topaz color. This yellow-brown quartz, usually sold as "topaz" by jewelers, is more correctly called citrine. Another quartz, a smoky-brown variety called cairngorm (to distinguish it from plain smoky quartz), also turns yellow-brown when heated, as the smokiness is driven off. Cairngorm is named after the mountain in Scotland where this variety of quartz first was found.

Heated Brazilian amethysts and cairngorm are the two main sources of citrine. Very little of the citrine you see is naturally that color.

92

Peridine

A green alteration of amethyst's purple is called peridine. It was discovered accidentally one day by workmen at an amethyst mine in the Minas Gerais district of Brazil. To cook their lunch, the workmen built a small fireplace of waste stones from the mine. After lunch the miners noticed that the stones had turned green!

Not all amethysts change color upon heating. Most of them merely fade out to white, then crack. But some turn yellow-brown and others turn green. No one knows why. Perhaps some day another accident will lead to the answer.

Amethyst and peridine crystals and cut stones.

Rose Quartz

In Custer, South Dakota, you can see a great pink-colored cliff 100 feet long. It is the core of a pegmatite of rose quartz. For decades this light-pink quartz was mined and sent to China, where it was carved into the delicate figures which are the delight of collectors of oriental carvings. Now the orientals get a clearer rose quartz from mines exploited in Brazil during World War II.

Rose quartz always is found in pegmatites in massive translucent blocks. A few small, rose-colored quartz crystals are found in pegmatites, but gemmologists are still not sure that the crystals are really the same material as the massive rose quartz.

All the latter type rose quartz is clouded with tiny needles of rutile, the same mineral inclusion that forms the star pattern in corundum. Some polished rose quartz also shows a six-rayed star, and for many years this quartz was used to make imitation star sapphires and star rubies. The stone was cut en cabochon, then painted on the back.

Rock crystal sometimes contains hair thick needles of rutile. Such stones, called *flèches d'amour*, "arrows of love," were popular in Victorian times. Another quartz which was popular in the last century was "quartz craqueleé" or "rubasse" quartz. It is a clear quartz which has been cracked by heating, then soaked in red dye.

Micro-crystalline Quartz

Micro-crystalline quartz usually is cloudy and nearly colorless or opaque and colored. It forms in rounded, layered masses and even beds, rather than in veins, pockets or seams. Quartz often forms these finely crystalline layered bands on the outermost edge of a geode, then for some unknown reason, completes its growth as coarse crystals.

There are many varieties of micro-crystalline quartz: chalcedony, carnelian, sard, blue chalcedony, amethyst chalcedony, chrysoprase, agate, moss agate, bloodstone, onyx, jasper, flint and chert. Neither flint nor chert, however, is used as a gemstone.

Chalcedony

Chalcedony is a general name for all micro-crystalline quartz except jasper, flint and chert. Pure chalcedony is light gray and translucent. Though it will be found in carvings, in its natural color it is not used much

94

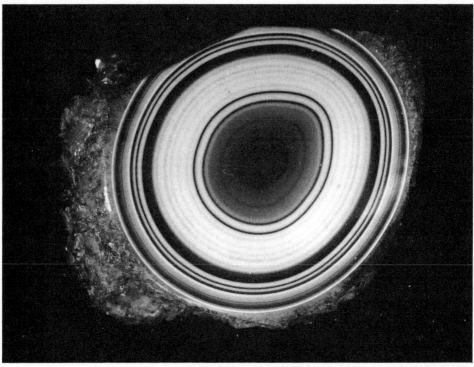

An agate slice.

as a gemstone. However, it forms the basis for many naturally colored or artificially dyed stones.

The red variety of chalcedony is called carnelian. An iron oxide impurity in the stone causes the red color. The ancient Egyptians carved cameos from carnelian. You can see them in museum collections. Many red and white Chinese carvings are white chalcedony which has been heated, the fire turning the outer layer a carnelian color.

The Chinese also carve blue chalcedony and violet, or amethystine, chalcedony. The source of Chinese amethystine chalcedony never has been disclosed, but a magnificent source of the purple stone recently was discovered in Mexico.

The most valuable chalcedony is chrysoprase. It is green, like jade, but it is a little cloudier than jade and slightly more opaque. Chrysoprase is the only chalcedony sold by the carat or pennyweight; the others are sold by the stone's dimensions (8 x 10 mm, 10 x 14 mm, etc.) or by the lot.

Ancient cameo of chrysoprase, the nickel-colored variety of chalcedony.

Nickel, a moderately rare metal, is the impurity which causes chrysoprase's jade-green color.

Agate

Agate is named after a river in Sicily where the stones were found in the days of Theoprastus, a Fourth Century B.C. Greek who wrote about stones. It is another variety of chalcedony. Ordinary agate is banded—that's how banded marbles, "agates," get their name. Moss agate and bloodstones are really translucent chalcedonies with inclusions. These inclusions are mineral salts—black, brown, green, yellow, pink or blue. When these salts form branching plantlike patterns, they are called moss agates. Stones which are mainly green with small red spots are called bloodstones. In medieval days bloodstones were believed to cure nose-bleeds.

You can find chalcedonies or agates almost anywhere—on a camping trip, a family picnic, a walk through the country or a trip to the beach.

96

The stones you find may not seem as brightly colored as those you see in jewelry stores. But this is because many onyxes and agates used for jewelry are dyed to intensify their colors.

Onyx

Onyx is another banded chalcedony. The Greeks named this stone with their word for "fingernail"—onyx—because the banding looks like the crescent near the base of the nail. Onyx-marble is also banded, but the soft construction stone, which may be used as a building facade, should not be confused with the hard quartz gemstone.

Black onyx is dyed chalcedony. The chalcedony is soaked in sugar syrup, then immersed in sulphuric acid, which blackens the carbon in the sugar, leaving a permanent insoluble color in the stone. Analine dyes and chemical salts are used to make yellow, red and blue onyxes. Usually these dyed onyxes are more translucent than the natural stones.

Jasper

When micro-crystalline quartz replaces some of the material in a rock and incorporates another part, the stone which results is a micro-crystalline quartz with a high proportion of impurities. Jasper, flint and chert are such quartzes. Jasper is colored yellow, brown, green or red, flint is gray to black, and chert is light-colored creamy gray or pink. Of these, only jasper is ever used as a gemstone.

The material which the quartz replaces and transforms may be petrified wood, a fossil, a dinosaur bone, even an asbestos or an iron ore.

98

14. Opal

PLINY, THE ROMAN NATURALIST, writes of a famous opal which was coveted by Mark Antony, who for a short time after Julius Caesar's death shared the rule of Rome. The opal belonged to a Roman Senator, Nonius. Antony offered Nonius money and favors for the jewel, and when these were refused, he threatened Nonius with banishment from Rome. To a Roman only death was a more severe punishment than exile from the world's greatest city. But Nonius chose exile—and the loss of all his property—rather than part with his opal.

Such devotion to opal is unlikely these days. In fact, for centuries opal was shunned as an "unlucky" stone. The superstition that opal is unlucky probably is based on the tendency of some stones to crack easily. For certainly it is bad luck when a lovely, costly gemstone cracks.

Stone Jelly

Opal breaks easily because of its special composition. Like quartz, opal is a compound of silicon and oxygen. But unlike quartz, opal is amorphous—it is the only inorganic gemstone without a crystal shape—and contains up to 10% water.

You might call opal a rigid stone jelly. This makes it a very fragile gemstone, for in a dry atmosphere, opal loses water, the jelly shrinks—and the stone cracks.

Opal is not only brittle but it is one of the softer gemstones, with a hardness of only 5½ to 6½. And it has the lowest refraction of any gemstone—1.45. However, the refractive index is unimportant for opals usually are cut en cabochon. Opal is one of the most exquisite gemstones and some of them are very valuable.

Opaque opal, called "common opal," has little value as a gemstone. Much more valuable is "fire opal," an orange, slightly cloudy stone found in Mexico. Fire opal is usually faceted.

The most valuable opal, however, is the silica (silicon and oxygen) jelly stone called "precious opal." This is the stone which gives off the stunning rainbow-colored reflections that are associated with opal. Until recently, nobody really knew what caused these reflections. Now, however, electron microscope studies have revealed a regular pattern of tiny spheres in the precious opal. These have the effect of a diffraction grating, breaking light into spectral colors. Common opal is made up of similar spheres, but they are not in regular array. Precious opal is always cut flat or en cabochon and polished to bring out the play of color.

Some opals reflect only greens and blues. The best stones, however, reflect the whole spectrum of colors—reds, yellows, greens and blues. These reflections assume several patterns. Look for them the next time you see an opal in a jeweler's window. If you see small points of color all over the stone, it is a "pin-fire" opal. If the stone's all-over color changes at once from, say, yellow to green to blue, as you change your vantage point, the stone is a "flash-fire" opal. A stone which reflects its fire in a more regular checkerboard-like pattern is an "harlequin" opal, so called after the costume of a carnival harlequin. Harlequin stones are considered the finest opals.

White and Black Opal

Hungary was the source of the earliest precious opals, milky white stones with patches of color. These stones are no longer found in Hungary,

Opals from Mexico.

but jewelers call any milky white precious opal "Hungarian opal," though most now come from Queensland, or South Australia.

Today Australia is the main source of all precious opal. The stones are found in sandstone, a sedimentary rock laid down on a former sea floor. Australian opals range from the milky Hungarian type from Queensland to "black opals," flashing stones with dark body color from New South Wales. Black harlequin opals (the blacker the better) with red and yellow fire are the most expensive of all opals.

There are a few sources of precious opal besides Australia. Brazil and Mexico also produce precious opals. The Brazilian stones are milky; the clear Mexican stones, called "jelly opals," show better in brooches than in rings. Mexico also is the source of the soft, translucent orange fire opals, which do not seem to crack as easily as the jelly opals do.

Precious opal is rarely found in the United States. Mines in Virgin Valley, Nevada, produce some lovely opals, but most of the stones crack in Nevada's dry air soon after they are mined. One of the few Virgin Valley stones that has not yet cracked is the famous dark brown, fiery "Roebling opal," named after its donor, a mineral collector of note and the builder of the Brooklyn Bridge. You can see this remarkable stone in the United States National Museum in Washington, D.C.

15. Diamond

RARITY IS ONE OF THE ESSENTIALS of a gemstone, so it seems strange that diamond, the "king of gemstones," is mined at a rate of four *tons* a year! About half a ton, or 1,000 pounds, of these diamonds are of gem quality. You can imagine how many diamonds that is when you consider that gemstones are weighed in carats and there are 183 carats to one troy *ounce!*

But rarity is relative, and it's fortunate that diamonds are so plentiful because they are in great demand. Yet, diamonds were not always so coveted. Before lapidaries learned how to cut these hard stones, you could exchange an amethyst for a diamond twice as large. Not anymore.

It is the combination of gemstone virtues which makes diamond the king. Ruby is hard, rock crystal is colorless, zircon has high refraction and dispersion—but only diamond combines all these qualities, each in the highest degree.

Diamond is also the only gemstone which consists of a single element, carbon. You will recall that diamond's extreme hardness comes from the closely packed arrangement of carbon atoms in the stone's cubic crystal lattice.

The Great Diamond Pipes

Although diamonds are mined in huge quantities today, man may have scratched only the surface of the still deeper but unattainable natural diamond deposits. Diamond crystals form in magma deep in the interior of the earth. A few crystals ride up along the tubes that feed some volcanoes and flow out with volcanic lava. When the lava decomposes, the hard diamond crystals remain behind in stream beds or on flat plains.

These are the stones which were discovered in India a few hundred years ago. Nobody bothered to ask how the diamond pebbles got there or from where they came. As the supply of diamonds dwindled, new deposits were mined in Brazil, then in Kimberley, South Africa. Then, rather suddenly, about seventy-five years ago, the discoveries of diamonds in Kimberley also fell. The miners had worked through the loose surface gravels and in some places, also through an underlying yellow, clayey rock. When a few fortunate miners in the yellow clay regions struck a soft bluish rock with their pick-axes, they were convinced that now their pits, too, were worked out.

Diamond crystals form in magma deep in the interior of the earth. A few crystals ride up along the tubes that feed some volcanoes and flow out with volcanic lava.

But two Englishmen, Cecil Rhodes and Barney Barnato, had been asking questions. And the answers they got convinced them that the small areas of bluish rock might very well be the original source of the Kimberley diamonds. So they bought up the various "worked-out" claims of individual miners and dug a shaft and tunnels deep into the blue rock.

Workers brought the blue rock to the surface, where it was broken up and spread over the ground. When the rock had decomposed enough, it was crushed further and hauled to a washing table—an inclined broad trough through which flowed running water. A thick layer of grease was spread on the floor of the trough. It had been found that the non-wetting,

Diamond-bearing concentrate is sluiced with water over a vibrating table with grease-covered terraces. Nonwettable diamonds stick to the grease, while other material is carried off as waste.

adamantine pebbles would stick to grease while the rest of the well-wetted dirt and rock would be washed away.

Rhodes and Barnato were right. The Kimberley blue rock is the tube extending down from an ancient volcano, and the solid lava was sprinkled with thousands of diamond crystals!

Half a century later, this "diamond pipe," as such a deposit is called, is still being mined. Nobody knows how far down the Kimberley diamond pipe extends, but workers already have tunnelled almost a mile deep!

The success of the Kimberley diamond mines started geologists hunting for diamond pipes all over the world. Some promising-looking pipes recently were discovered in Canada. The Russians have found diamond pipes in eastern Siberia, near the Arctic Circle. And geologists believe

Diamonds scraped from surface of grease table, then immersed in kettles of boiling water to clean off the grease.

they have uncovered the original pipes which were the source of the diamonds in India hundreds of years ago.

There is a blue-ground diamond pipe in the United States near Murfreesboro, Arkansas. The stones are of good quality, but the high cost of labor and the divided ownership of the land make extensive mining prohibitive. The largest diamond ever found in America, a 40-carat stone, came from Arkansas. For a fee, you can hunt for your own diamonds in the Murfreesboro pits. The chances of finding a large stone are small, but if you go often enough and look hard enough, and are lucky, you may find one.

The Glacial Diamonds

About sixty diamonds have been found scattered in glacial debris. These stones were deposited by the huge glacier that covered northern

North America more than twenty thousand years ago. As the great ice sheet slowly retreated northward, it left behind tons of gravel, earth and clay, and some diamond pebbles.

Since these glaciers originally formed in the north, the source of these diamonds may easily be the volcanic pipes which recently were mapped in Canada. Other random finds have been made in West Virginia, Georgia and Alabama. Their source is unknown.

A glacier descended in North America 20,000 years ago. As the ice sheet retreated northward, it left behind tons of gravel, earth, clay, and some diamond pebbles.

Famous Diamonds

Although diamonds are abundant, large ones are rare. That's why a 1-carat diamond costs four times as much as a ½-carat stone, and a 2-carat diamond costs about four times as much as a 1-carat stone.

The really large diamonds can be counted on the fingers of your hand. Many of these diamonds are Indian stones which have passed from one owner to another, often through theft, murder or the fortunes of war. The famous 186-carat Koh-i-noor diamond, for instance, passed from one warring Indian rajah to another until 1526. In that year, the Moguls, sweeping into India from China, conquered all the rajahs and seized the Koh-i-noor. When the Persians conquered the Moguls two hundred years later, the Koh-i-noor was removed to Persia, where it changed hands through a succession of assassinations and intrigues. Runjit Singh, the Lion of the Punjab, retrieved the Koh-i-noor from the Persians, and he surrendered it to Queen Victoria in 1849 when the British conquered India. Unfortunately, Queen Victoria had the Koh-i-noor recut. The re-cutting alone cost $40,000 and robbed the stone of almost half of its weight.

The largest rough diamond ever found weighed 3,106 carats, a little over a pound! It was discovered in 1905 in the Transvaal and was named the Cullinan diamond, in honor of the chairman of the mining company that owned it. The Cullinan diamond eventually was presented to King Edward VII of England, who had it cut into gemstones. One of these stones, the 530-carat, pear-shaped "Star of Africa," is the largest cut diamond in the world.

"Fancy Diamonds"

Richly colored diamonds are called "fancy" diamonds. Yellow and brown stones are fairly common; blue, green, orange and pink stones are rarer, and rarest of all is a ruby-red diamond. The famous 44-carat Hope diamond (named after a former owner) is a blue stone. You can see it in the United States National Museum in Washington, D.C.

The Hope diamond is almost certainly a part of a larger blue stone which Tavernier, a famous traveler who wrote about gemstones, brought from India in 1642. Tavernier's stone, which was sold to King Louis XIV in 1668, disappeared when the French crown jewels were stolen in 1792.

In its original form it has not been seen since. But in 1830, the Hope diamond together with a smaller blue stone of the same hue appeared on the London market. Are they the pieces of Tavernier's stone? Nobody knows for sure, but the probability is great that they are.

You may have heard diamonds described as "silver cape," "cape" and "dark cape" stones. These are diamonds with tints of color ranging from light yellow to distinctly yellow. So-called "premier" diamonds are named for a mine in the Transvaal which produces a high proportion of them. Premier diamonds are strongly fluorescent. In ultra-violet rich daylight they look bluish, but under artificial light they look yellow or brown.

Fancy diamonds also can be created by "bombarding" the dark-colored cape or brown stones with the beam from a cyclotron or by placing them in an atom pile. The new colors—canary-yellow, gold, red-brown, green, greenish-blue, or chartreuse—are more acceptible and salable than the cape tints which the jeweler is likely to disparage as "off-color."

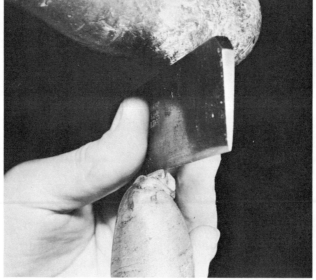

DIAMOND CUTTING

1. CLEAVING *After groove is made in the stone, holder is set upright in another rigid holder. Cleaving knife is held in groove. If the stone has been properly marked and grooved, a light tap on the knife by a wooden mallet or steel rod will split the diamond cleanly in two along the cleavage plane. A miscalculation can shatter the diamond into bits.*

Diamond Cutting

Only a diamond cuts a diamond. To cut and polish the half ton of gem-quality diamonds which are mined annually requires another half ton of diamonds. Large irregularly shaped stones, however, are first cleaved. And since the diamond crystal cleaves only in one crystal direction, diamond cutters must be careful to choose the right direction, otherwise the stone might shatter. When the huge Cullinan stone was cleaved, the man in charge, who had a weak heart, arranged for an ambulance to stand by, in case he had miscalculated the Cullinan's cleavage directions and the stone should shatter!

COURTESY OF N. W. AYER & SON, INC.

DIAMOND CUTTING

2. SAWING *When a diamond is to be divided against its cleaving grain, it is sawed. The stone is set in solder in a metal dop, which is clamped into an arm above the saw. The saw blade, 35/1000ths of an inch thick, its edge impregnated with diamond dust, then revolves at high speed against the diamond. It takes hours to cut through even a small diamond.*

DIAMOND CUTTING

3. ROUNDING *After a diamond has been sawed, the operation that gives it a standard round, or "brilliant," cut, is known as rounding. The sawed part is set into a holder and mounted on a lathe; another diamond, set into the end of a long stick, is held against it, as the lathe revolves at high speed. The result is a diamond perfectly round at its diameter or "girdle".*

After a large diamond is cleaved, it is sawed as nearly as possible to the rough shape of the finished stone. Ideally one-third of a diamond should be above the stone's widest point, or girdle, and two-thirds should lie below it. Small diamond octahedrons are not cleaved; sawing is the usual first step in cutting them.

For a round brilliant, "bruting" is the next step—rubbing the diamond against another diamond to round off the corners of each stone. Then the stone's facets are polished on a lap, or grinding wheel. Diamond laps are made of porous iron which catch and hold diamond dust.

The Unseen Diamonds

Diamonds that you never see are among the most valuable. They are the stones used in industry for grinding and cutting. Almost every product you use has been manufactured with the help of diamonds—automobiles, bicycles, wires, screws, etc.

110

DIAMOND CUTTING

4. POLISHING, *the final step in diamond cutting. The stone is set into a dop and held down against a revolving iron disk. To produce the diamond's flat surfaces, or facets, the disk is coated with a mixture of oils and diamond dust. Variations of even a fraction of a degree in the polishing can reduce the brilliance of the finished diamond.*

All electrical equipment—refrigerators, toasters, radios, television sets, even light bulbs—depend on diamond dies. These are flat diamonds through which a small hole has been drilled. Thick metal rods are pulled through tinier and tinier holes until they are drawn into the fine wire used in electrical equipment and filaments.

Diamond drills are used by dentists; diamond-studded core bits are used to bore deep into the earth's crust in man's continual search for oil; and diamonds are used to make the great rockets which eventually will propel man to the moon.

Indeed, there is no limit to the usefulness, as well as the beauty, of this valuable gemstone.

16. Pearl, Coral and Amber

PLINY THOUGHT THAT PEARLS were formed by dewdrops falling into open oysters. It is a charming idea but not true. Actually a pearl begins when a tiny fish, a worm, or perhaps a grain of sand slips into the fleshy part of an oyster, irritating it in much the same way your eye is irritated by a cinder in it. Your eye secretes tears which usually wash out the irritant. But the oyster, unable to rid itself of the irritant, smooths it with a coating of concentric layers of a secretion composed of the same material as the lining of its shell. Over a period of years of continued secretion a pearl is formed.

Any oyster, clam or mussel can form a pearl in this way, but only those mollusks which secrete an iridescent, mother-of-pearl substance called *nacre* form valuable pearls. Without a lustrous nacre, a pearl is dull and of no value as a gemstone.

The pearl itself is composed of many thin layers of calcium carbonate (aragonite) held in a net of organic cartilaginous material called conchiolin. Aragonite is soluble in acid, which makes pearls vulnerable to the acid in perspiration. You have to treat pearls carefully. Cleopatra is said to have dissolved a pearl in wine to impress Mark Antony with her wealth. If the Egyptian Queen's wine was acidic enough, her pearl indeed may have dissolved—but it might have taken a few weeks. Had she drunk it often, she wouldn't have needed the asp!

Not all pearls are round. You may have seen oval or pear-shaped pearls in earrings, or pearls called "baroques," a word derived from the Portuguese *barrôco*, which means "irregularly shaped pearl." Round pearls are considered the most valuable shape because they can be used for necklaces. But pearls are judged by color, luster, iridescence (called the "orient") and size as well as shape, and the pearls in a necklace must be properly matched in every respect. Sometimes it takes 20 years to complete the matching for a strand of fine pearls.

Fresh-Water Pearls

The earliest pearls came from mussels living in the rivers of Europe, Asia and America. Fresh-water pearls are a delicate pink, for the mussel's

The Canning Jewel, a pendant dated about 1580, made in India from gold, enamel and various stones. The body is formed from a large baroque pearl.

shell is pink. Unfortunately, these pearls are neither as abundant nor as popular as they used to be. Contamination of rivers by industry has killed many of the mussels, while the success of "cultured" pearls has reduced the value of all natural pearls.

But you never know when you will stumble upon a treasure. One of the largest fresh-water pearls ever found was fished from a river near Paterson, New Jersey, years ago, when its waters were still clean. It weighed 93 grains (pearls are sold by the grain; 4 grains equal one carat).

Oriental Pearls

Oriental pearls, the most valuable of all pearls, are found in the warm waters of the Persian Gulf and the South Pacific. The pearls form

114

in an inedible salt-water oyster of the *Margaritifera* genus. South Pacific Margaritifera grow larger than those in the Persian Gulf, and some of them have black-edged and gold-edged shells. Such shells can produce golden pearls and the so-called "black" pearls, which are not really black, but dark gray or bronze-colored.

Pearl oysters are collected sometimes systematically, sometimes haphazardly, at pearl fisheries. The principal fisheries lie off the shores of Australia and such islands as Borneo, New Guinea, Ceylon and Bahrein in the Persian Gulf. At Bahrein, native divers pluck the oysters from prescribed areas of the off-shore oyster beds, covering each area only once every six years—the least time for a good-sized pearl to form.

Pearl oyster beds usually are about 40 feet deep. Some divers can stay under water for about two minutes at a time collecting the oysters. In dangerous water, they may carry a weapon to ward off sharks.

The oysters are hauled up to a boat in baskets and put into sacks. At Bahrein these sacks are auctioned off to pearl-buying syndicates, which open the decaying oysters. One oyster in two or three may yield a pearl, but good ones are rare.

Any pearls which are found are sent to Bombay, India, the center of the pearl trade. In Bombay, the pearls are cleaned, bleached, graded and resold to gem merchants all over the world.

Oriental pearls, like fresh-water pearls, are rare, and they are becoming rarer. The main reason for the decline in the supply of oriental pearls is loss of value following the development of the "cultured" pearl, plus disease that wiped out the Ceylon beds, political problems and a changing way of life even in primitive lands.

Cultured Pearls

Most of the pearls you see in jewelry stores are "cultured" pearls. They are pearls which are also made naturally by oysters—but with a little boost from man. The boost consists of providing a large enough irritant which stimulates the oyster to form a pearl, and gives it a head start on size.

For many years the Chinese, and then the Japanese, tried to form pearls by introducing foreign objects such as tiny buddhas and strings of beads into a mollusk's shell. Often the mollusk died, but sometimes it formed a shell around the object. These half-pearls are known as *mabes*.

115

Then, in the early 1900's, the Japanese succeeded in introducing tiny beads of mother-of-pearl into the fleshy part of nacre-secreting oysters. The pearls the oysters produced looked as natural as oriental pearls. Nobody noticed the difference between the two pearls until one of the Japanese pearls was cut in half in Paris around 1912, revealing the original mother-of-pearl bead. This discovery caused an uproar in the gem trade. There was a court battle over whether the Japanese pearls should be called "artificial," "imitative" or "cultured." A French court settled on the term "cultured."

Cultured pearls have taken much of the chance out of pearl finding and are grown in great numbers, so they are less costly. But no one need be ashamed of a necklace of fine cultured pearls. Cultured and oriental pearls are so similar that the usual way of finding the difference between them is with X-rays.

Japanese carving of precious pink coral. Pieces this size can be obtained only from the base of a large branch.

Coral

Coral is the hard base on which grow colonies of tiny marine animals. It is composed of calcium carbonate, the same substance which constitutes pearl.

The type of coral that forms reefs is white and porous, the tiny holes indicating where the animal itself lived. You often see specimens of reef

116

coral in souvenir shops, often shockingly dyed. Gemstone coral, however, is pink to red, and it is compact because the animal lives further outside the shell than the reef-building animal does.

Gemstone coral is rare. It grows in single, isolated branching "trees" in warm seas, particularly in the Mediterranean Sea and the Sea of Japan. Coral fisheries are worked in much the same way that pearl fisheries are. But they are systematically worked, divers take the coral from the same spot only every tenth year instead of every sixth year as pearl divers do.

The base of a coral tree is seldom more than 2 inches thick, so only small gemstones can be shaped from coral. Usually coral is carved into delicate figurines or small beads. In the United States, the most valuable color is ox-blood red, but the Japanese prefer a clear pink. A so-called black coral has been found in Hawaiian waters, but outside of Honolulu you seldom see it in jewelry.

Amber

Amber is resin that oozed from the trees of 40 or 50 million years ago. At that time the earth was probably uniformly warmer than it is today. Forests and jungles covered the vast continents. Resin oozing from those trees collected in big drops, just as it does today in our evergreen forests, and fell to the ground, where it was buried among the litter of the forest floor.

Insects in amber. Ants trapped in the soft gum which hardened while it clung to the trunk of a pine tree, were covered by a second gush of gum, to be preserved for 50 million years and changed to amber.

117

Gradually, over millions of years, the earthen floor of what was to be East Germany sank and was buried in sediments. Still younger beds of rock were laid down on top of this basin. The pressure squeezed and hardened the rocks and the buried resin.

Then, the Earth's crust warped and was partially raised, with the North Sea flooding only a part of the basin. Rivers and streams washed away the overlying beds of rock, exposing on valley and cliff edges the hardened resin, now amber. As waves lapped at the margins of submerged and broken cliffs, the light amber floated away in sea water. These rounded, water-worn chunks of amber were eventually washed ashore in Germany, England, Denmark, Latvia and Lithuania. East Germany was later discovered to be the source of amber, and though still found along the shore, it is also mined from those soft rocks which once lay under ancient seas.

Amber also is found in Sicily, Canada, Rumania and Burma. Copal and kauri gum, resins much like amber but not as hard because they are recent secretions, are found on the forest floors of Africa and New Zealand. These soft resins are used in varnishes.

Early European peoples used amber as a jewel and as a ceremonial incense, for amber gives off a pleasant piney scent as it smolders. The early Greeks noticed that if you rubbed amber against the fur of an animal the amber attracted dust or pieces of fiber. Twenty centuries later this magnetic effect was found to be caused by friction-generated electricity—the word "electricity" coming from the Greek word for amber, *elektron*.

Today amber is cut into beads and decorative carvings. True amber is yellow-brown; any other color in this gemstone is the result of dyeing. Not all amber is clear, however; some is cloudy and even opaque. Occasionally a tiny insect is found in an amber drop—trapped there forty million years ago when the resin was still sticky. What scientists know about prehistoric insects is partly derived from a study of such casts which are our best insect fossils. Judging from the specimens which have been found, insects have not changed much in forty million years.

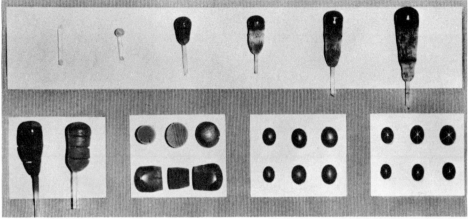

Growth of star, starts with seed rod (TOP LEFT) *and boule grows layer by layer in individual oxyhydrogen furnace.* (TOP ROW) *Boules in various stages of growth.* (2ND ROW LEFT) *Boules sawed into blanks. They vary in shape because ruby is cut from boule in two directions—end-to-end and side-to-side—whereas sapphire is cut side-to-side only.* (2ND ROW, THIRD AND FOURTH FROM LEFT) *Blanks, rough-ground and finished stones.*

17. Imitation and Synthetic Gemstones

IMITATION GEMSTONES HAVE a long history. Among the bright green emeralds from Cleopatra's mines exhibited in museum gemstone collections are a few that have not worn so well. Examination reveals that they are glass—green glass molded into the six-sided crystal shape of the emerald! One wonders if the original owner knew what he was getting.

The Greeks and Romans also made imitation gems from glass, and today the practice continues. As a material for imitating gemstones, glass has several strong points, the principal one being its cheapness. It also is transparent, attractive and easily molded. But in faceted stones glass is not very brilliant, does not take a good polish and is not very hard.

Synthetic Rubies and Sapphires

For centuries man sought a better imitation of gemstones than glass. With the emergence of chemistry, men found that minerals consisted of compounds of various elements, and they attempted to fabricate gemmy

119

A growing star boule.
Aluminum oxide powder is passed through an oxyhydrogen furnace, where it is
melted. It is then recrystallized on a seed to form a boule. Incandescent light occurs
when star powder passes through flame and a boule is growing.

equivalents in the laboratory, using the proper elements. It was more difficult than it sounds, for it takes great heat, sometimes using pressure as well to fuse these elements together to make a gemstone.

Then, in 1891, a French chemist named Verneuil invented a burner hot enough to melt corundum. His idea was to melt down small ruby chips and recrystallize the mass into a larger single ruby. But this proved too difficult; impurities bothered him. So Verneuil prepared a powder of pure aluminum oxide and chromium—the elements of a ruby—and dropped it through the flame of the burner. The powder melted and crystallized into a small round mass of red corundum—a ruby!

The French called these round masses boules, which is French for "balls." The name perists even though today synthetic gemstones crystallize as cylinders, starting from a bit of sapphire rod or "seed."

Cutting boules into blanks.
Boules first mounted in pitch on small blocks of wood, then cut on a diamond wheel into blanks.

Star boule segments, or blanks, being mounted on dop sticks or steel shafts. This provides a way of positioning the crystal until it is shaped.

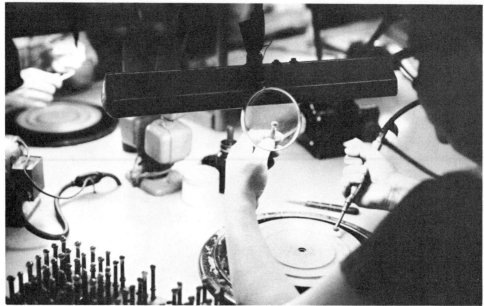

Polishing rough-ground stars with diamond dust abrasive. Star on dop stick is turned at end of a flexible shaft.

In 1947 the Linde Company produced synthetic star rubies by the Verneuil process. A large amount of titanium oxide, or rutile, the impurity which forms the rays of the star, was melted with the chromium-doped aluminum oxide. Subsequently the boule was kept at a constant temperature, near its melting point, while the rutile separated out to form the star. Experts had said it couldn't be done, but Linde did it.

Linde synthetic star sapphires are so perfect that gem merchants who once fought them now say of a fine natural stone: "It's almost as good as a Linde."

Spinel Synthetics

Spinel also can be synthesized by the Verneuil process. In fact, synthetic spinels are made in various colors and wrongly sold as synthetic sapphires, zircons, tourmalines, peridots and aquamarines. A colorless spinel is sold as an imitation diamond.

COURTESY OF UNION CARBIDE CORPORATION

Grading stars for color and quality.
Devices used to check accuracy in size shown at lower left.

To make certain that stone is centered when laid flat on its base, individual templates are used for each size of stone and adjusted until star is centered. Back of stone is then ground off flush with the flat of the template.

Most synthetic sapphires you see in jewelry stores actually are synthetic spinels with a sapphire blue color! Spinel is easier to synthesize than corundum; colors dissolve in it more readily, it has a lower melting point and it is easier to cut.

Synthetic Emeralds

For years chemists also attempted to synthesize emeralds. But only a few minerals like corundum and spinel resume their crystal shape after

124

they have been melted by the Verneuil process. Beryl does not. You can melt an emerald to a bubbly green mass, but when it cools, it remains a bubbly green mass. Chemists learned this through sad experience.

Finally, in 1935, Carroll Chatham, a San Francisco chemist, succeeded in synthesizing commercial-sized emeralds. He claimed to have done so by duplicating as nearly as possible the natural conditions under which emeralds form. This involved dissolving the chemical ingredients of beryl in a molten solution and allowing the beryl to crystallize out of the solution during slow cooling.

The Linde Company wanted to grow emeralds too. After some experimentation they marketed a new synthetic emerald, grown from a watery solution under high pressure in a closed container called a "bomb". This process is very close to what nature actually does. Linde's stones have many of the minor properties of a natural emerald, unlike the stones grown by Chatham or rubies grown by the Verneuil process.

Man even has made a gemstone that does not exist in nature! It happened somewhat accidentally. While making Linde star sapphires, chemists tried melting just the titanium oxide to let it crystallize in the Verneuil process. Subsequently the addition of strontium, a rare metallic element, produced strontium titanate, a brilliant, light-colored stone with a higher dispersion than diamond, marketed under the name fabulite, which is whiter than its predecessor, titania.

Is It Real or Not?

It is unlikely that you could distinguish a well-made synthetic gemstone from a natural one, without special equipment. It takes an expert to keep from being fooled, for synthetics that approximate the chemical composition of natural gemstones also approximate their physical properties. But there are differences between synthetic and natural stones which you can see with the aid of a microscope.

If you study a natural crystal under a microscope, you can see the straight lines and angles of the layers of the crystal's growth. A close look at a boule, or even a cut Verneuil-grown synthetic gemstone, shows curved lines instead.

In light-colored stones, the lines of growth are difficult to distinguish. But you can tell the natural stone from the synthetic one by studying the tiny bubbles present in almost all stones. The bubbles in natural stones are angular; those in boule-synthetics are round or drop-shaped.

A more difficult synthetic stone to recognize is the Chatham emerald. Since it makes angular crystals, it has no curving growth lines. It so resembles a natural emerald that an expert must make a careful examination or a test before he can distinguish between the two stones. One of the tests requires ultraviolet light. Few natural emeralds glow red under ultraviolet light, and none glow as brilliantly red as Chatham or Linde synthetic emeralds.

The Art of Imitation

Although synthetic stones are the most nearly perfect substitutes for natural gemstones, other methods of imitating gemstones flourish.

One of the most ingenious bits of gem fakery involves brilliant green "jadeite" cabochons from Hong Kong. The cabochon actually is three separate pieces of pale translucent jade. The top and bottom fit perfectly, like a box. The middle piece, which is a lens-like disc, fills the opening with a jelly-like green dye, filling in all the open space. The result is a stone with the color, translucency and specific gravity of valuable jadeite. You have to look on the bottom for the joints where the pieces are cemented together to discover the imitation.

A similar, but simpler, principle underlies opal "doublets." A thin plate of brilliant but transparent opal is joined with black cement to a backing of glass, onyx or common gray opal. Opal doublets look like black precious opals. The only sure way to tell the difference between the two stones is to look for the cemented joint around the edge. Today one has to watch out for black-dyed, poor quality opal, too.

Pearl imitations usually are glass beads coated with a paint called pearl essence or *essence d'orient*. The glass beads are threaded on short lengths of wire and repeatedly dipped in the paint. Often you find a loose flap of paint near the drill hole. Imitation pearls (but not cultured pearls) also are softer to the teeth. Some are excellent; there is a great variation in quality in these imitations. The cheap ones are just silvery and soon turn yellow; the good ones have some of the iridescence of true pearls.

126

Gemstones of the Future

As the world's supply of natural gemstones slowly dwindles, synthetic stones (as distinct from simple imitations) become more important. Even the diamond, king of gemstones, has been synthesized. In 1955, the General Electric Company subjected pure carbon to tremendous heat and pressure in specially-built giant presses and produced tiny diamond crystals. The process has been refined, and crystals up to two carats have been grown, but synthetic diamonds still are suitable only as an abrasive dust.

What does the future hold? Surely man eventually will make gem-quality diamonds—and many other gemstones—himself. And he will discover new deposits of natural gemstones, perhaps even new gemstones, in the ground, under the sea or in outer space. No one can predict even the possibilities, for nature is full of surprises and man is gifted with curiosity. Who knows, perhaps the next chapter in the fascinating story of gemstones will be written by a reader of this book. I hope so.

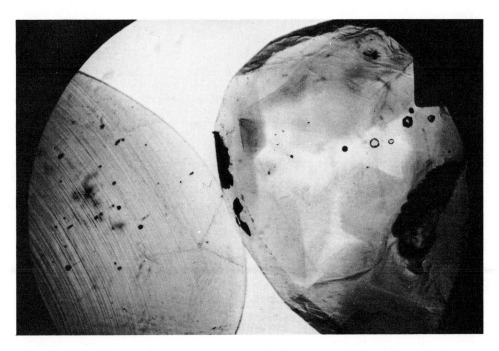

Microscopic study of genuine and synthetic rubies. (LEFT) *Curved lines of synthetic.* (RIGHT) *Layers of crystal growth of genuine ruby with angular bubbles.*

Characteristics of Gem Stones used in Jewelry

EXPLANATION OF SIZE: Small—to 5 carats. Medium—to 50 carats. Large—over 50 carats.
EXPLANATION OF COST: Low—to $5 a carat. Medium—to $100 a carat. High—to $1,000 a carat.

NAME	COMPOSITION	COLOR	RESISTANCE TO WEAR	PRACTICAL SIZE	COST
DIAMOND	Carbon	White to brown and fancy colors	Excellent	Any	High
RUBY	Aluminum oxide (Corundum—sapphire)	Red	Good	Small	Very high
SAPPHIRE	Aluminum oxide	Blue	Good	Medium	High
FANCY SAPPHIRE	Aluminum oxide	Yellow, pink, white, orange, green, violet	Good	Medium to large	Medium
STAR RUBY and SAPPHIRE	Aluminum oxide	Red, pink, violet blue, gray	Good	Medium to large	High to low
SYNTHETIC SAPPHIRE or RUBY	Aluminum oxide	Yellow, pink, blue, red, etc.	Good	Up to 20 cts.	Low (Stars—Medium)
SPINEL	Magnesium aluminum oxide	Red, blue, gray, lilac, orange	Medium	Medium	Medium to low
SYNTHETIC SPINEL	Spinel	Blue, white, light blue, yellow, gray, green, alexandrite colors	Good	Up to 40 cts.	Low
EMERALD	Beryllium aluminum silicate (beryl)	Green	Poor	Medium	Very high
SYNTHETIC EMERALD	Beryl	Green	Poor	Small	High
AQUAMARINE	Beryl	Blue-green to light blue	Good	Any	Medium
GOLDEN BERYL	Beryl	Yellow-green to golden	Good	Any	Medium
MORGANITE	Beryl	Pink to rose	Good	Any	Low to medium
TOURMALINE	Complex silicate	Red, pink, green, blue, wine, brown, yellow	Fair	Green—any size Red—to 50 cts. Others—medium	Medium

128

NAME	REFRACTION	REFRACTIVE INDEX	MOST LIKELY DOUBLE	RECOGNITION CHARACTERS
DIAMOND	Single	2.42	Zircon, titania, spinel—syn.	High index, single refraction, cut and luster
RUBY	Double	1.77	Synthetic	Inclusions and shape of flaws
SAPPHIRE	Double	1.77	Synthetics incl. spinel	Inclusions, double refr., dichroism.
FANCY SAPPHIRE	Double	1.77	Synthetics, glass and doublets	Inclusions, double refr., refr. index
STAR RUBY and SAPPHIRE	Double	1.77	Star quartz, synthetic stars	Appearance of back, color on side view
SYNTHETIC SAPPHIRE or RUBY	Double	1.78	Synthetic spinel, glass	Double refraction, refractive index
SPINEL	Single	1.72	Synthetic sapphire, garnet	Refractive index, single refraction, inclusions
SYNTHETIC SPINEL	Anomalous Double	1.73	Spinel, sapphire, aqua., topaz alexandrite	Weak double refrac., lack of dichroism, refractive index
EMERALD	Double	1.58	Soldered emerald, glass, tourmaline, peridot, green garnet, synthetic emerald	Emerald filter dichroism, refractive index, inclusions
SYNTHETIC EMERALD	Double	1.56-8	Genuine emerald	Flaws, fluorescence
AQUAMARINE	Double	1.58	Synthetic spinel, blue topaz	Double refraction, refractive index
GOLDEN BERYL	Double	1.58	Citrine, quartz, precious topaz, glass, doublets	Refractive index, double refraction
MORGANITE	Double	1.58	Kunzite, tourmaline, pink sapphire	Refractive index
TOURMALINE	Double	1.63	Many stones	Double refraction, refractive index

Characteristics of Gem Stones used in Jewelry

EXPLANATION OF SIZE: Small—to 5 carats. Medium—to 50 carats. Large—over 50 carats.
EXPLANATION OF COST: Low—to $5 a carat. Medium—to $100 a carat. High—to $1,000 a carat.

NAME	COMPOSITION	COLOR	RESISTANCE TO WEAR	PRACTICAL SIZE	COST
PRECIOUS TOPAZ	Complex silicate	White, blue, golden, pink	Fair	White & blue—any size Gold&pink—to medium	Low to medium
GARNET	Variable silicates	Reds, brown and green	Good	Reds too dark when large Greens to 6 cts.	Low to high
ZIRCON	Zirconium silicate	White, blue, brown, yellow, green	Poor	Small to medium	Low to medium
PERIDOT	Iron magnesium silicate	Yellow-green, brown	Fair	Any	Medium
CHRYSOBERYL	Beryllium aluminate	Yellow, green, brown	Good	Medium	Medium
CAT'S-EYE	Chrysoberyl	Greenish to brownish	Excellent	To large	High
ALEXANDRITE	Chrysoberyl	Green by day Amethyst by night	Good	Russian (small) Ceylon (medium)	High
OPAL	Hydrous silica	Color flashes in white, gray, black or colorless	Poor	Large	Low to high
QUARTZ	Silica	*Transparent:*			
		Colorless—rock crystal	Good	Large	Low
		Purple—amethyst	Good	Large	Medium
		Brown—quartz topaz, citrine	Good	Large	Low
		Pink—rose quartz	Good	Large	Low
		Smoky—cairngorm	Good	Large	Low
		Translucent:			
		Striped—agate	Good	Large	Low
		Spotted—moss agate	Good	Large	Low
		Uniform—onyx-chalcedony	Good	Large	Low
		Opaque:			
		Uniform or spotted—jasper	Good	Large	Low
FELDSPAR	Alkali silicate	Opaque, green—amazonstone	Fair	Large	Very low
		Blue sheen—labradorite	Fair	Large	Low
		Translucent, white—moonstone	Fair	Large	Low
TURQUOISE	Copper aluminum phosphate	Blue	Fair	Large	Low
JADE	Complex silicate	Green, red, black, mauve	Good	Large	Low to very high

130

NAME	REFRACTION	REFRACTIVE INDEX	MOST LIKELY DOUBLE	RECOGNITION CHARACTERS
PRECIOUS TOPAZ	Double	1.62	Beryl, aquamarine, quartz topaz	Refractive index
GARNET	Single or Anom. double	1.74 to 1.88	Spinel, synthetic, glass	Single refraction Inclusions, refractive index
ZIRCON	Double (Strong)	1.79 to 1.98	Diamond, synthetics	Double refraction, wear on facet edges
PERIDOT	Double (Strong)	1.68	Tourmaline, Chrysoberyl, glass	Strong double refraction Low dichroism
CHRYSOBERYL	Double	1.75	Tourmaline, peridot	Refractive index
CAT'S-EYE	Double	1.75	Quartz	Gravity and transluc.
ALEXANDRITE	Double	1.75	Synthetic imitations	Dichroism, inclusions in synthetic sapphire
OPAL	Single	1.45	Glass	Color changes
QUARTZ	Double	1.55	Glass	Refractive index and
	Double	1.55	Glass	double refraction
	Double	1.55	Glass	Color patches in ame-
	Double	1.55	Glass	thyst and citrine
	Double	1.55	Glass	
		1.54	Glass	Crystalline bands
		1.54	Glass	
		1.54	Glass	Bubbles in glass
		1.54	Glass	Appearance, luster
FELDSPAR		1.53	Jade	Cleavage, sheen
		1.56	Brazilian butterfly	
		1.53	Glass or white onyx	Blue sheen
TURQUOISE		1.61	Glass or composition	Difficult if matrix not present
JADE		1.65 to 1.68	Onyx or glass, serpentine	Luster of polished surface

131

Books for further reading

Anderson, B. W., *Gem Testing*, Temple Press, London, 7th Ed., 1964, pp. 377.

> The best work on the identification of stones, with introductory chapters on instruments and techniques, followed by detailed descriptions of the various stones. Highly recommended.

Bignami-Moneta, Speranza Cavegnago, *Gemmologia*, Hoepli, Milan, 2nd Ed., 1966, pp. 1390.

> A costly but sumptuous volume in Italian, replete with color illustrations. In spite of the language difficulty, the American reader will find it a useful reference work, remembering that technical terms are similar in all languages. Highly recommended for real specialists.

Kraus, Edward Henry, and Slawson, Chester Baker, *Gems and Gem Materials*, McGraw-Hill, New York, 3rd Ed., 1939, pp. 287.

> A standard text for gemmology courses, the American equivalent of *Gemstones and Their Distinctive Characters*, by Herbert Smith. Not as useful as the latter, since it covers less ground, though equally authoritative.

The Lapidary Journal, San Diego, California (P.O. Box 2369).

> A handsome monthly journal for amateur cutters and collectors, replete with practical information, locality data, reports of new developments and advertisements of suppliers. Recommended highly for the hobbyist.

Liddicoat, Richard Thomas, *Handbook of Gem Identification*, Gemological Institute of America, Los Angeles, California, 7th Ed., 1966, pp. 426.

> Recommended moderately.

Smith, G. F. Herbert, *Gemstones and Their Distinctive Characters*, Methuen & Co., Ltd., London, and New York, 13th Ed., 1958, pp. 560.

> Standard British work, the best single volume, reasonably priced book in English. Testing methods and the various stones, varieties and sources are authoritatively discussed.

Webster, Robert, *Gems*, Butterworth's, London, 1962, 2 vols., pp. 792.

> The most authoritative book on gemstones in English. Vol. I describes the various stones and Vol. II is devoted to testing methods. A costly work and therefore recommended only for the serious student.

132

Glossary

agate. A multi-colored microscopically crystalline, variegated chalcedony, one of the many varieties of quartz. It may be banded, irregularly clouded, or have visible impurities as in moss agate.

Alaska black diamond. Hematite.

alexandrite. Found originally in the Urals and since in Ceylon, it was named in honor of Alexander II of Russia. A variety of chrysoberyl which because of its unusual absorption changes color in different lights. It is green in daylight and wine-red in most artificial lights.

allochromatic. Refers to the coloring caused by minor impurities of stones, which, if pure, would be colorless. Few stones are idiochromatic (colored by essential ingredients).

almandine (al'man-deen). An iron aluminum garnet (a misnomer for violet spinel), which is often used as a gem, when it has a purplish red color. The name derives from Alabanda.

amazonite. Or Amazon stone, an old name, referring to the Brazilian deposits. A green variety of potash feldspar known as microcline, frequently found in pegmatite dikes.

amber. A fossil resin, the preserved gum of coniferous trees. Comes mostly from East Prussia, though Burma, Roumania, Sicily, New Jersey and Canada have produced similar resins. Insects which were entrapped as the gum exuded have been preserved and their shells are to be seen in finished pieces of amber.

amethyst. A purple variety of coarsely crystallized quartz. The origin of the color is unknown. A popular gem which comes in many shades, the deepest, often called Russian or Uralian amethyst, being the most desirable.

amorphous. "Without form," meaning that there is no regular internal arrangement of molecules; as opposed to crystalline, in which there is such an arrangement.

andradite (an'dra-dite). A calcium-iron garnet; red, yellow, brown, green or black. Topazolite is pale green or brown; demantoid a brilliant green and the most valuable of the garnet group.

anisotropic (an'ice-o-trop-ik). The opposite of "isotropic," means that light does not pass through in different directions at the same speed. Anisotropic substances have the property of breaking light up into rays vibrating in different directions and traveling at different speeds.

aragonite (a-rag on-ite). A form of calcium carbonate and an important constituent of the pearl, its use is widespread as a non-gem material.

asteria, asteriated, asterism. Refers to the property possessed by some gemstones when cut cabochon or when viewed in transmitted light, of reflecting the light as a star, or surrounding the light source with radiating rays.

aventurine (av-ven't your-een). A name with many applications. Originating with the accidental Italian (aventura-chance) discovery of this effect. As applied to quartz, it refers to a green variety of quartzite which contains flakes of green mica. Aventurine feldspars, such as sunstone, contain flakes of hematite which reflect light in certain postions.

axis. The theoretical center of motion of an arbor or other rotating object. A crystallographic axis is an imaginary line passing through the center of an ideal crystal, and parallel to the intersections of the principal faces.

baguette (bag-ett′). A small diamond or other gemstone which is rectangular in shape.

Balas ruby. A misnomer for red spinel. From Balascia, a synonym for Badakshan, No. Afghanistan, which furnished the best stones in the Middle Ages.

ballas. Rough diamonds in rounded shapes, unsuitable for cutting as gems but very valuable for industrial uses. They have a confused, intergrown internal structure which makes cleaving through them impossible, and consequently, they are tougher than usual diamonds when used as tool tips.

baroque pearl (ba-roke′). Pearl of irregular form.

birefringence (bye′ree-frin′gence). The separation by a doubly refracting crystallized substance of single rays of light which have been broken into two rays and made to vibrate in two planes at right angles to each other, moving at different speeds.

blueground. The fresh rock of the diamond pipes, in which the diamonds occur.

blue white. Term, often misused, to describe the color of a diamond. It includes anything from a Jager to a Silver Cape, since bluish glints in dispersed light tend to counterbalance the body color of all grades except Capes and Yellows.

bort. Also spelled boart, boort, bortz and bowr. An old French word meaning bastard, and applied to low quality diamonds either the poorest quality, usable only for cutting purposes, or to all diamonds of non-gem quality.

boulder opal. Brown iron oxide nodules containing opal-filled fissures, found in the opal beds of Queensland, Australia.

brilliant. A type of cutting, used especially on diamonds wtih 58 facets. A synonym for a brilliant-cut diamond. There are 32 facets, plus the table, above the girdle, and 24, plus the culet, below.

bruting. A process in brilliant cutting of diamonds which involves rubbing two stones together to round their corners before faceting. Same as shaping or girdling.

buff top. A low cabochon type of cutting, the top just slightly rounded.

cabochon (kabb-o-shon′). An unfacetted form of cutting; the stone is given a rounded convex shape, and cut high or low as is best for the desired effect. Cat's-eyes and star sapphires are cut in a high cabochon to bring out the eye or the star; moonstones and opals are best cut low.

cairngorm (kairn′gorm). Smoky quartz. A popular Scottish stone named for a mountain in the streams of which waterworn crystals are found. It is smoky gray or brownish in color, not to be confused with the yellow citrine.

calcite (kal′site). Calcium carbonate, a common mineral and the principal constituent of limestone and marble. Also known as Mexican onyx, Mexican jade, Atlas pearls, calcite prism pearls and cerulene.

calibre (kal′i-bray). Small colored stones in rectangular or square shapes used adjunctively in the decoration of a piece of jewelry, rather than as the central motif, or set in bands in guard rings.

cameo. A stone, which has been carved so that a raised image in one color stands out from the background of another color. Stone cameos are principally cut from a variety of flat-banded agate, dyed and known as onyx or sardonyx. Shell cameos are cut from shells with similar colored layers.

canary diamond. A fancy diamond with a strong, pleasing yellow color. The Tiffany diamond, a square-cut brilliant of 128.5 carats, is the largest known canary diamond.

cape. A color grade of diamonds. The third and fourth grades, with a slight yellow tint, are known as first cape and second cape, respectively. First white and white precede this group; first bye and second bye are the grade below capes.

carat. A unit of weight for gemstones. Comes from the name of a seed, which was first used as a weight, but there is uncertainty about the exact origin; it may have been the Greek "keration," or the African "kuara." Although it has varied from time to time, the now generally accepted standard is the metric carat, which is equivalent to 200 milligrams, or one-fifth of one gram; to 3.08647 grains Troy, and to 0.00705478 ounces avoirdupois. Not to be confused with karat, which is a term denoting the ratio of fine gold in an alloy.

carbuncle. Any cabochon-cut red stone, such as ruby, spinel, garnet. Most generally used with reference to a cabochon-cut garnet.

carnelian. Sometimes spelled cornelian. A reddish-brown, orange-brown on yellow-brown variety of chalcedony whose color is caused by iron oxide. Used in inexpensive jewelry and in carved Chinese objects. It grades into sard with increasing brown tones.

cat's-eye. A gem which, when cut cabochon, shows a single light streak across its face. It is caused by innumerable parallel inclusions, of minute needle-like crystals or of tubular cavities, the sides of which reflect light. Cat's-eyes are known in many stones, but the unmodified word refers to chrysoberyl.

chalcedony (kal-sed'o-ny). A microscopically crystalline variety of quartz forming in transparent to translucent masses; gray, white, blue, brown, black, etc. Trade name for a natural blue "onyx."

chalchihuitl (chal'chi-hwee'tl). A Meixcan term for any stone which has been carved into a decorative or useful object. It usually refers to jadeite or turquoise, but sometimes to porphyry or serpentine.

cleavage. A property possessed by many crystallized substances, of breaking readily along certain planes, with a resultant flat surface. Different minerals have different cleavages, their positions depending upon their internal molecular structures. Diamonds cleave parallel to the octahedral faces, as does fluorite.

coated stones. Rough diamonds which are naturally coated with a thin colored layer. In cut stones it refers to the attempt to conceal a yellowish tinge by coloring the girdle or the entire stone with a thin blue layer.

Colorado goldstone. Name under which brown aventurine glass is sold in Colorado.

commercially perfect. Term applied to first piqué diamonds; i.e., diamonds with slight (vvs) imperfections.

commercial white. Common white diamond with a slight yellow tint.

crown. Upper part of a gem.

crystal. A naturally angular shape,

bounded by plane surfaces which are related to the internal molecular structure. They possess certain elements of symmetry and are grouped into six systems based upon these elements.

crystalline. The internal structure of a solid, in which the molecules are in a definite arrangement in relation to one another. Crystalline substances possess certain properties related to their internal structure; these properties remain unaltered regardless of whether or not there is an external shape, or crystal, which reflects the internal molecular arrangement.

demantoid (demm'an-toyd). A bright green variety of andradite garnet incorrectly known as: Bobrowka garnet, Siberian chrysolite, Uralian olivine, and Uralian emerald. Rare in larger sizes, though frequent in small stones, and generally sold under the name of "olivine," it is among the most attractive of gems, with a high index of refraction, and stronger dispersion than a diamond.

dichroism (di'kro-ism). The property possessed by many crystallized substances of transmitting (or conversely, absorbing), different colors of light in different directions through the crystal.

dichroscope (die'kroe-skope). An instrument, consisting of a calcite rhomb, for the detection of dichroism in a gem. It separates the two vibration directions of the light passing through a doubly refracting gem, and by placing them side by side, permits accurate color comparisons.

dimorphism. Crystallization of a chemical compound into two different crystal forms.

dodecahedron (do'deck-a-hee'dron). Crystallography. One of the more common forms of the cubic system, having 12 lozenge-shaped or rhombic faces.

double refraction. The division of transmitted light into two rays traveling at different rates on different paths and vibrating at right angles to each other.

doublet. Any imitation or manufactured stone of two component parts. A glass imitation with a thin layer of genuine garnet fused on the top. When viewed through the back the deep red color of the garnet only shows at the edge of the stone.

emerald cut. One of the principal types of facet cutting, the other being brilliant cut. In this cutting, commonly used on emeralds, the elongation of the rectangular facets is parallel to the girdle. The finished stone tends to be square or rectangular.

emerald filter. A piece of colored glass.

fancy color diamond. Any gem diamond not included in the usual commercial color ranges of whites, light yellows and light browns.

fancy sapphires. Corundum gems of any color except blue or red.

fire. The rainbow flashes of light reflected from within a stone. Fire depends upon the dispersion of the gem as well as upon the refractive index, the color and the cutting.

floating opal. Opal chips in glycerine, enclosed in a glass sphere.

fluorescence (flew'or-ess'sense). The property possessed by some substances of changing and reflecting invisible ultra-violet light rays as longer visible wavelengths of light. Diamonds often fluoresce blue; willemite is usually a brilliant green under ultra-violet rays.

Gem. A stone cut and polished for use in jewelry, which fulfills the requirements of beauty, durability and rarity. Word is frequently used to signify a fine stone of unusual quality and sometimes as a prefix to indicate rough from which a good stone could be cut, as "gem crystal."

gem color. The perfection color of any specimen.

gemology, gemmology. Derived from the Latin: "gemmas." The scientific, historical and legendary study of gem minerals as distinct from all the minerals scientifically studied in mineralogy. The American spelling uses but one "m," the preferable British spelling uses two.

geode (jee′ode). A crystal-lined nodule of stone; frequently occurring in agate and amethyst. The nodules are often harder than the rock in which they occur and, after weathering, are found as round, hollow boulders.

granite. A fairly coarsely crystalline rock composed essentially of potash feldspar and quartz, usually with a few accessory dark minerals like mica.

graphic granite. An intergrowth of large crystals of quartz and feldspar found in pegmatites, in which the quartz crystals are so arranged that their cross-sections resemble cuneiform writing.

habit. Crystallography. The overall appearance of a crystal. An elongated beryl crystal is said to have a prismatic habit, the usual diamond crystal to have an octahedral habit.

hessonite (hess′on-ite). The name for the yellowish to reddish-brown variety of grossular garnet, derived from a Grecian word for "less," referring to its hardness in relation to the brown zircon hyacinth, with which it is perpetually confused.

hyacinth (hi′a-sinth). Orange, red and reddish-brown zircon, also used, not

unjustifiably, for yellow and brown zircon.

idiochromatic (id″ee-o-kro-mat′ic). Mineral coloration due to essential elements of the composition of the mineral rather than to chance impurities; the pigments of most gems. Turquoise and lazulite are examples of idiochromatic gems.

index of refraction. Refraction is an optical property of any translucent substance; the index is a measure of the amount that light passing from air into the transmitting substance is bent.

indicolite. Light or dark blue tourmaline, one of the rarer colors of the gem. Also known as Brazilian sapphire.

industrial diamonds. Diamonds usually unsuitable for gem purposes because of flaws or poor color, which are used in industry because of their superior hardness over all other materials.

interference colors. These are the colors in a birefringent substance under examination between crossed polarizing devices. The actual colors observed are of significance only in relation to other grains, of the same size, of other substances, for the colors vary according to the strength of the birefringence and the thickness of the grain.

istotropic (eye′so-trop″ic). Not birefringent. Light passes through an isotropic substance in all directions at the same speed. Isometric minerals, glass and other amorphous substances are isotropic.

karat. One twenty-fourth part by weight of the metallic element gold in an alloy. Pure or fine gold is 24 karats; 18 karat gold (abbreviated 18 K. or 18 Kt.) consists of 18 parts of pure gold, mixed with 6 parts of other metal; 14 karat gold (abbreviated 14 K. or 14 Kt.) is 14 parts of pure gold, combined with 10 parts of other metal; etc. Word is probably derived from the Greek, "keration," a seed used in ancient times for weighing gold.

Kashmir sapphire. Theoretically, cornflower blue sapphires from the Zanskar range of the northwestern Himalayas in Kashmir, but, as generally used, the name for any sapphire of fine quality.

lap. A horizontal spinning wheel about 18 inches in diameter against which gems are polished. Diamond laps are composed of soft iron, which best retains the diamond dust that is doing the actual cutting, and they rotate at high speeds—2000 to 2400 revolutions per minute.

lapidary (lap′i-dare-ee). A person who cuts and polishes gems, except diamonds. In older usage, a treatise on gems was called a lapidary.

light brown. A commercial color classification of diamonds, a distinctly brown stone which lies between fine light brown and brown in quality.

melee (mell′ee—anglicized pronunciation). The embellishing diamonds mounted in any article or jewelry are collectively classed as melee. Derived from French word for "mixed," now generally applied in the diamond industry to round diamonds, whether graded and sized or not (single, Swiss or full-cut), up to 1/6, 1/5 or even 1/4 ct. in size.

Moh's scale. A scale of relative hardness for use in testing minerals. Named for the German mineralogist Friedrich Mohs (1772-1839). The minerals are numbered, but the intervals between them are very different.
The scale is:

1. TALC
2. GYPSUM
3. CALCITE
4. FLUORITE
5. APATITE
6. FELDSPAR
7. QUARTZ
8. TOPAZ
9. CORUNDUM
10. DIAMOND

A copper penny is about 2¾, a fingernail 2½, a fine steel knife about 6. Minerals vary in hardness in different crystal directions.

moldavite (mole′dav-ite). A light green glass of natural but unexplained origin, found along the Moldau in Bohemia, hence its name.

Montana sapphire. A blue sapphire, lighter and more steely in color than the Kashmir and Ceylonese.

naturals. Unpolished surfaces of the original diamond crystal faces which may often be seen along the girdle. If visible elsewhere, the stone is considered imperfect.

obsidian (ob-sidd′ee-an). A natural glass, formed when lava solidifies too rapidly for any of the constituents to crystallize. It is often translucent, sometimes iridescent or adularescent (having a bluish sheen).

odontolite (o-dont′o-lite). "Bone turquoise," an iron impregnated, blue-colored fossilized bone, which resembles turquoise. Some of the best has come from the tusks of mammoths found in Siberia. The structure of the bone, visible in polished surfaces, enables an easy distinction from the true turquoise.

old mine cut. Originally descriptive of the high-crowned, small-tabled, square or cushion-shaped brilliant cut diamonds, in vogue during the 19th century, which retained much of the original outline and weight of the octahedron rough at the sacrifice of brilliancy. Because stones so cut came from Brazil and India, they were called "old mine" to distinguish them from diamonds from the newer South African mines

optic axis. The direction in a crystal along which no double refraction is observed. In hexagonal and tetragonal crystals it is parallel to the long axis, in the other birefringent systems there are two optic axes, inclined at varying angles to each other.

padparadscha, padmaradschah, padparajam. Adapted from the Singhalese word for lotus-colored "padmaragaya," it applies to the synthetic orange or pinkish-orange corundums.

pavilion. In American and British nomenclature, the lower side of a cut stone; on the Continent, the pavilion is the upper side.

pegmatite. A coarsely crystalled residual magma mass, usually in the form of a dike or a lense, resulting from the slow solidification of a deep-seated igneous intrusive, such as often results, for example, in the formation of granite.

perfect gemstone. A gemstone which, when examined by a trained eye under a diamond eye loupe or other magnifier of not less than 10-power, discloses no flaw, crack, carbon spot, cloud, or other blemish or imperfection of any sort.

plane polarized light. Light which has passed through a polarizing medium, such as a nicol prism or a sheet of Polaroid, and as a result all of its vibrations are in parallel planes.

pleochroism (plee'o-kro"ism). A difference in color seen in many (anisotropic) gems when they are viewed in different directions. Best observed with polarized light or through an instrument like a dichroscope.

precious stones. The more valuable stones used in jewelry, as distinguished from semiprecious. Diamond, ruby, sapphire, emerald and pearl are classed as precious stones, and cat's-eye, alexandrite, black opal and topaz (not citrine) are also frequently so classed. All others are usually considered semiprecious.

premier oillies. Typical stones of the Premier mine, with a blueish fluorescence visible even in daylight, which gives them an opalescent appearance, but the true body color may be distinctly yellow and the quality lower than stones which have none of the blueish fluorescence.

reconstructed ruby. Michaud in 1890 and for some years thereafter made gemstones out of fused fragments of ruby. At first they were highly valued but by 1904 their price had fallen greatly. It is incorrect to use this term for synthetic ruby.

refraction. The deflection from a straight path suffered by a beam of light when it passes from one medium into another of greater or lesser density. The more the rate of travel is slowed, the greater the amount of refraction.

refractometer (re'frac-tom"met-er). An instrument for measuring the index or indices of refraction of a substance. There are many such instruments, some for liquids and some especially designed for gemstones.

semiprecious stone. The less valuable of the two classes into which gemstones are arbitrarily divided. Diamond, emerald, ruby, sapphire and pearl are grouped as precious stones, because the value of fine specimens is always high and the demand for them is constant; cat's-eye, alexandrite, black opal and topaz are also frequently classed as precious.

All other gemstones are usually considered semiprecious, for one or more of the following reasons: comparative

139

abundance, relative softness, inferior brilliance, unfamiliarity to the public, or the whims of fashion.

single cut. A primitive form of brilliant cutting, fashioned from the rough octahedron by truncating the corners and placing a table and culet on the stone, 18 facets in all.·

single refraction. Transmitted light that is not broken up, but passes through the crystal with all its vibrations at the same speed, since all directions are alike to it.

spectroscope. An instrument which breaks the transmitted light up into a spectrum. It can be used in the identification of gemstones by comparison of the absorption in different color bands in unknown gems, wtih the absorption in known stones.

spessartine (spess′ar-tine). A manganese aluminum garnet of a brownish-red to orange-brown or yellow-brown hue. Uncommon and rare in gems of any size.

sugar stone. Pyrite. The compact white to pink datolite from the Michigan copper district.

synthetic. A term applied to an artificially made substance which has all the physical properties and the chemical composition of a natural substance. Synthetic gemstones should be sharply distinguished from imitation stones; the former are physically and chemically identical with the natural material, while the latter are similar only in appearance.

table diamond. An early form of diamond cutting, the octahedral point being worn down to square, the opposite point to a very small plane and the sides squared up, the width of the two sides together equaling the upper plane surface.

trichroism. The more accurate term for dichroism, when dealing with mineral crystallizing in the orthorhombic, monoclinic and triclinic systems. It refers to the three different colors observed in colored minerals, in the different optical directions.

trilling. A type of twinning in which three crystals are intergrown according to regular laws; chrysoberyl trillings are best known to gemologists.

twinning. An intergrowth of two or more crystals, or parts of crystals in reversed relationship to each other, in accordance with a mathematical law. It is caused by an actual reversal of atomic positions in the crystal lattice,

Verneuil, A. A French chemist, who, in 1891, invented the method still used today to manufacture synthetic sapphires and rubies. Using a powder of the desired composition and an oxyhydrogen flame, he succeeded in melting the aluminum oxide in a series of drops which built up the boules of the synthetic gems.

yellow diamond. The lowest diamond color classification; yellow, but not yellow enough to be a fancy diamond.

yellow ground. The oxidized upper portion of the diamond pipes; with depths, oxidation ends and the matrix rock becomes blue ground.

*This glossary was adapted from material previously written by the author for *The Jewelers' Dictionary* second edition 1950, published by *The Jewelers' Circular-Keystone,* a Chilton publication.

Index